Body Building
for Beginners

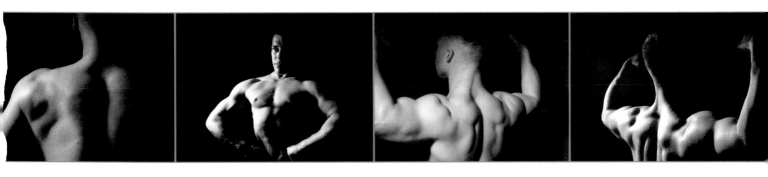

Body Building
for Beginners

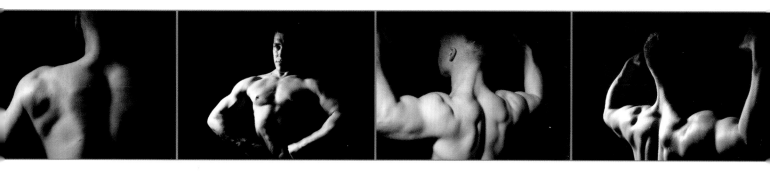

Grant Griffiths

Published by SILVERDALE BOOKS
An imprint of Bookmart Ltd
Registered number 2372865
Trading as Bookmart Ltd
Blaby Road
Wigston
Leicester LE18 4SE

© 2004 D&S Books Ltd

D&S Books Ltd
Kerswell,
Parkham Ash, Bideford
Devon, England
EX39 5PR

e-mail us at:-
enquiries@dsbooks.fsnet.co.uk

This edition printed 2004

Book code DS0070. Body Building

ISBN 1-856057-77-1

Creative Director: Sarah King
Project editor: Anna Southgate
Photographer: Colin Bowling
Designer: 2H Design

Typeset in Optima and Franklin Gothic Heavy

Printed in China

1 3 5 7 9 10 8 6 4 2

Contents

Introduction

Having passed the three stages of weight training you are now at a peak of development and performance. You have developed skills and honed your physique. You enjoy going to the gym or exercising at home at regular intervals, while pushing your body to higher physical levels. You have learned that your own body is the best possible gauge for you to understand your own physical level of fitness. This being the case, you will obviously be looking for a new challenge. True weightlifting might now be your way forward, whether you see this as a way into sporting competition or just as a way of providing yourself with a new and exciting goal.

If body building is to be considered seriously, then the term must be understood in its widest sense. A knowledge of the human body is necessary, and this includes an understanding of the bony system and the joints as well as the musculature. You need this in order to perform every activity safely and with the maximum benefit to your physical potential. The first chapter of this book deals with this aspect of body building.

The second chapter focuses on training plans and offers guidelines for fitness, motivation, thought and movement. The chapter ends with a series of suggested exercises.

Chapter Three deals with the next level up and is for people who are extremely determined and serious about their efforts. Powerlifting is physically demanding and requires thorough concentration and effort. The text looks at the basic principles of powerlifting, paying particular attention to the factors that might affect motivation, the training and preparation. Again, the chapter ends with a series of suggested exercises.

Your Anatomy

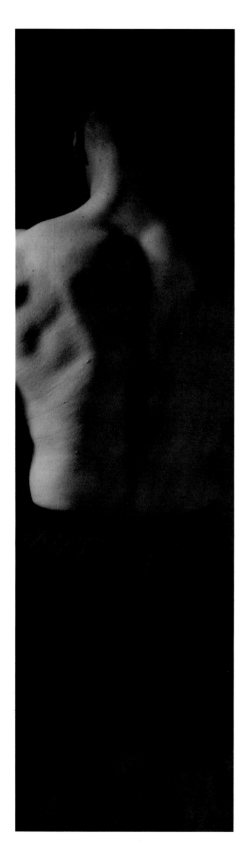

Before commencing with a detailed study of the bones, joints and muscles of the human body, it will be useful to have a closer look at the term 'human anatomy'.

If the term is considered in its broadest sense, it will be found to cover the various structures of the body and the factors that influence the structures. However, it will soon be realised that such a broad topic would cover far too wide a field to meet the needs of the potential lifter or trainer. So we'll take advantage of systematic anatomy, which as the name implies, arranges the various structures in a number of systems or groups in accordance with the functions they perform.

To meet the immediate needs of yourself and your trainer it is intended to deal in detail with three such systems:

a)   osteology or the bony system

b)   arthrology or the joints

c)   myology or the muscular system

The Bones

By way of introduction to the detailed study of the bone system let's consider a few general points in outline.

The skeleton is a framework comprising a series of bones and cartilage. Many of these bones have both definite and combined functions to perform. For example, there are those which support the weight of the body; those which give protection to underlying structures such as vital organs; those which perform the function of levers; and those which provide a surface for the attachment of muscle.

Classification of Bones

Bones may be divided into four classes:
a) long
b) short
c) flat
d) irregular

a) Long bones are found in the upper and lower limbs, and they function as levers. Each possesses a shaft and two ends. Usually the ends are expanded for the purpose of articulation (forming joint) and muscular attachment.

b) Short bones can be located on the hands and feet, for example, where strength, compactness and reasonably restricted movement are needed.

c) Flat bones are usually found where the basic requirement is to protect underlying structures or to provide a broad surface for muscular attachment. In the latter case the scapula or shoulder blade is an obvious example.

d) Irregular bones, as the term implies, covers those bones which present varied features, for example, the innominate bones of the pelvic girdle.

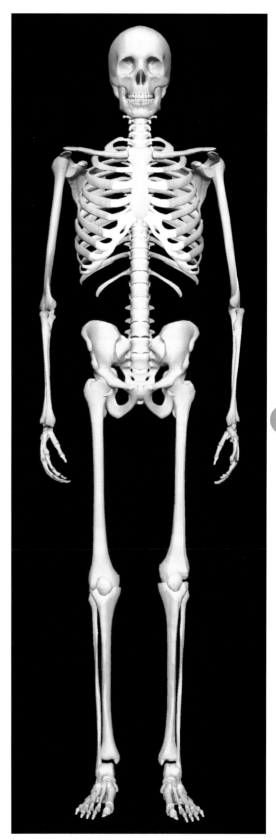

9

Bones of the Lower Limbs

The bones of the lower limbs are connected to
the torso by means of the pelvic area.

The bones comprising this group are:

Feet (phalanges, metatarsals, tarsals)

Tibia

Fibula

Patella

Femur

Pelvic girdle

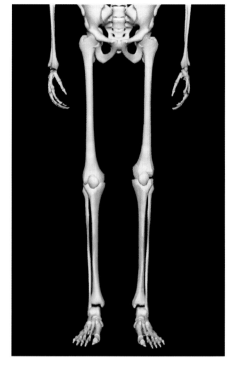

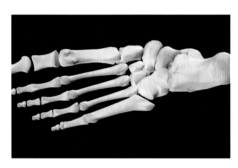

The Feet

The fourteen phalanges of the toes
are shorter than those of the hand.
The five metatarsal bones lie
behind the phalanges and in front
of the tarsals. The seven tarsals lie
behind the metatarsals, and there
are two of particular interest, the
talus and the calcaneum. The talus can be described as the main
connecting link between the feet and bones of the lower leg; it also plays
an important part in the formation of the ankle joint. The calcaneum or
heel bone of the tarsal group, has the insertion of the common tendon of
the calf muscles.

The Tibia

The shin bone or tibia is the innermost bone of the lower leg and is the
stronger of the two leg bones. It possesses a shaft and two ends; excluding
the femur, it is the longest bone of the skeleton.

The upper end of the tibia forms a joint with the lower end of the femur.
As a general feature, it is expanded in shape to afford a good surface for
the body weight to be transmitted through the lower end of the femur. The
shaft is triangular in section, and in the lower part is found a sharp crest,
better known as the shin. The lower end is also expanded and articulates
both with the fibula and talus in the formation of the ankle joint.

The Fibula

The fibula is the outermost bone of the lower leg, and is quite slender
compared with the tibia. The upper end is slightly expanded and
articulates with the outer condyle (a rounded joint) of the tibia; it is
important to note that it does not articulate with the femur. The shaft,
being very slender, functions mainly for the attachment of muscles. The
lower end projects further down than the level of the tibia and, with the
tibia, it articulates with the talus in the formation of the ankle joint.

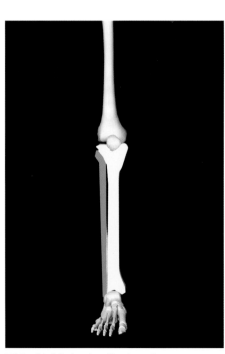

*Tibia (highlighted yellow) and
fibula (blue).*

10

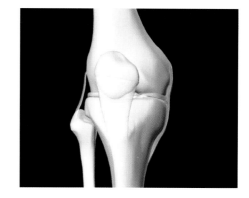

The Patella

The patella is better known as the knee cap. It is flat and triangular in shape and is found within the tendon of the quadriceps muscle group. It enters into the formation of the knee joint by means of an articulating surface on the femur.

The Femur

The femur or thigh bone is the longest and strongest bone in the body. The upper end or head is semi-spherical and fits into the cup-shaped hollow on the hipbone, known as the acetabulum, and thus forms the hip joint. Other general features are the greater and lesser trochanters which are roughly shaped processes. The shaft is rounded in shape; on the posterior surface is a well-marked ridge called the linea aspera to which a number of muscles are attached. The lower end is expanded to provide a good bearing surface for transmission of the body weight through the upper surface of the tibia; this end also enters into the formation of the knee joint.

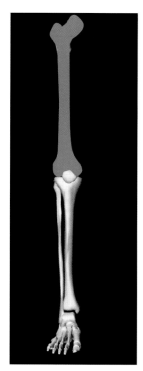

The femur

The Pelvic Area

The pelvic girdle is formed by the two innominate bones and wedged between them are the sacrum and the coccyx. The innominate bones are irregular in shape and are composed of three conjoined bones, the ilium or hipbone, the pubis in front and the ischium. The ischium is the most posterior bone and should be familiar because we sit on it.

At the upper end the ilium is quite expanded, and forms the iliac crest, and there is also an articulating surface for the sacrum. The pubis, which forms the front part of the hipbone is somewhat triangular in outline; the ischium, which forms the lower part of the hipbone, is well known to us as it is this bone that we sit upon.

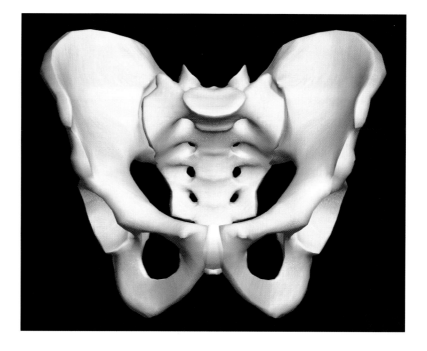

The common factor between all three bones is that they enter into the formation of the cup-shaped cavity called the acetabulum. This receives the head of the femur, thus forming the hip joint.

The sacrum and coccyx will be described in the section dealing with the spine.

Bones of the Upper Extremity

The bones of the upper extremity are attached to the torso by means of the shoulder girdle, which consists of the clavicle and the scapula. The bones in this group are:

Hand (phalanges, metacarpals, carpals)

Ulna

Radius

Humerus

Clavicle

Scapula

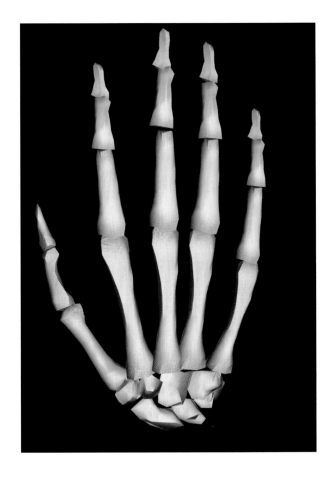

The Hand

The fourteen phalanges refer to the fingers; the five metacarpals enter in the formation of the palm; and the eight carpals form the bones of the wrist.

The Ulna

The ulna is the innermost bone of the forearm. The upper end has two features of particular interest, the olecranon process and the coronoid process. The olcranon process is found on the uppermost part of the upper end and is shaped like a beak. It fits into the depression called the olecranon fossa of the lower end of the humerus when the elbow is extended. The coronoid feature fits into the coronoid fossa of the humerus when the elbow is flexed; this feature is shaped like a bracket. Finally, the lower end articulates with the humerus and radius in the formation of the elbow joint. The shaft is triangular in shape, giving attachment to the muscles which pronate and supinate the forearm, and also to those which control the movement of the wrist and fingers. The lower end is slightly expanded and comprises a rounded head which articulates with the inner side of the lower end of the radius entering into the radio-ulna joint; the styloid process is a short, rounded projection which is found on the lower end of the ulna.

The ulna

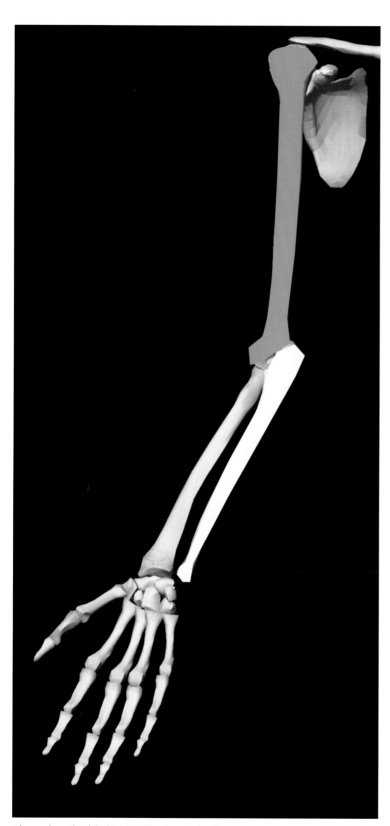

The radius (highlighted yellow) and the humerus (blue).

The Radius

The radius is the outermost bone of the forearm; it is shorter at the head than the ulna. The upper end is expanded, but is narrower than the lower end, presenting a disc-shaped head which articulates with the humerus on its upper surface and with the ulna at the sides. A general feature to note is the biceps tubercle (a smaller process) to which the tendon of the biceps muscle is inserted. The shaft is triangular in section, rather narrow above but widening rapidly towards the lower end. The lower end is the widest part of the radius, entering into the formation of two joints: firstly, two of the carpal bones enter into the formation of the wrist joint and, secondly, the head of the ulna enters in the formation of the inferior radio-ulna joint.

The Humerus

The humerus is the longest and largest bone of the upper limb. The upper end comprises a semi-spherical head and two broad, rough features called tuberosities. The head articulates with the glenoid cavity of the scapula in the formation of the shoulder joint. Below the head is a slightly constricted part known as the anatomical neck. The greater tuberosity is found to the outer side, and below the neck, and the lesser tuberosity is found at the front. The well-known bicipital groove separates the two tuberosities. The shaft is rounded in its upper part, but becomes triangular on section to almost the lower end of the bone. On the back of the shaft is a groove for the radial nerve, and on the outer side, a little above the middle, is the deltoid tuberosity connecting with the deltoid muscle. The lower end is broad and flat, articulating with the radius and ulna in the formation of the elbow joint. General features include the coronoid fossa, which receives the coronoid process of the ulna when the elbow is bent, and the olcranon fossa, which receives the olcranon process of the ulna when the elbow is extended.

13

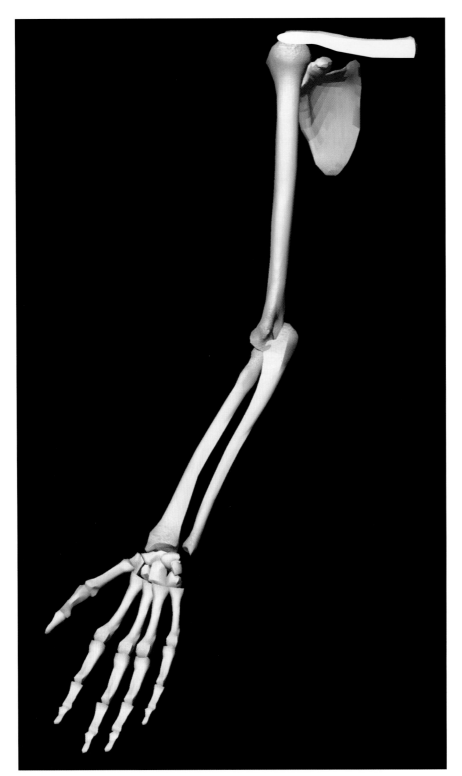

The Clavicle

The clavicle, or collar bone, is a long, gently curved bone that forms the anterior part of the shoulder girdle. Generally speaking, it acts as a prop to brace the shoulder back, and to transmit some of the weight of the limb to the trunk. There are two ends, the inner or sternal end, which articulates with the sternum in the formation of the sternoclavicular joint, and the outer, or acromial extremity, which articulates with the acromion process of the scapula in the formation of the acromio-calvicular joint.

The Scapula

The scapula forms the posterior part of the shoulder area; it is a large and flattened triangular bone covering parts of the second to the seventh ribs. The scapula presents several interesting features:

(1) The two surfaces: the anterior or coastal surface is found to lie nearest the ribs, and the posterior, or dorsal surface, which can be easily distinguished by its prominent ridge of bone, is termed the spine of the scapula;

(2) The three angles: the superior angle lies at the junction of the superior and vertebral borders; the inferior angle is the lowest point of the scapula and lies over the seventh rib (when the arm is raised it can be seen to pass forwards round the chest wall); and the lateral angle is thick and broad and can be located in the section bearing the glenoid cavity;

(3 The three borders: the superior border is thin and sharp and is the shortest of the borders (it extends from the superior angle to the base of the corocoid process); the vertebral border extends from the inferior to the superior angle; the axillary border extends from the inferior angle to the glenoid cavity.

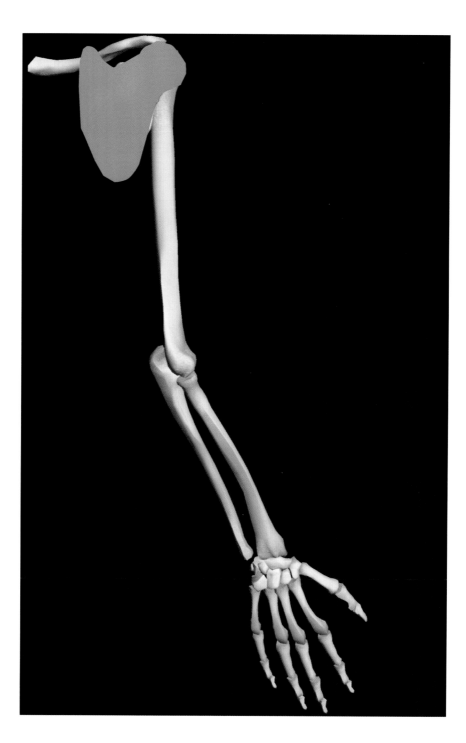

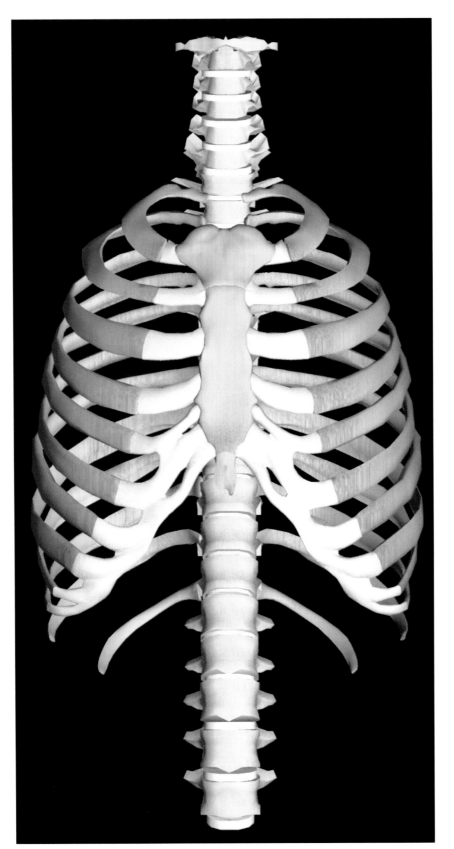

16

The Thorax

The thorax is formed by the twelve thoracic vertebrae at the back, the twelve pairs of ribs at the sides and the sternum at the front.

The sternum or breast bone is a long, flat bone comprising three parts. The manubrium sterni is triangular in shape and is placed above the main body. It articulates at the upper and outer sides with the sternal ends of the clavicles. At the sides proper, the first pair of ribs articulate with the manubrium, and the second pair articulate at the junction of the manubrium and the body of the sternum. The body of the sternum is narrower and longer than the manubrium with which it articulates at the sternal angle. At the lower end it narrows and articulates with the xiphoid process. The sides are notched for the attachment of the third, fourth, fifth, sixth and seventh ribs. The xiphoid process is the smallest part and sometimes it varies in shape.

The thoracic vertebrae are dealt with in detail under the section on the spine, but in this context it should be noted that they form part of the thorax by affording facets and transverse processes on the vertebrae to which the twelve pairs of ribs are attached.

The Ribs

Each rib has two ends and a shaft. There are twelve pairs of ribs and they are classified according to their anterior attachments, i.e. true, false and floating.

The upper seven pairs of ribs are termed the true ribs. These are attached behind to the thoracic vertebrae and to the sternum anteriorly by means of their costal cartilages. The lower five pairs are termed false ribs, and are attached to the sternum indirectly by means of the costal cartilages to the cartilage of the rib immediately above. The two lowermost ribs are termed the floating ribs, so-called because they are free at their anterior ends.

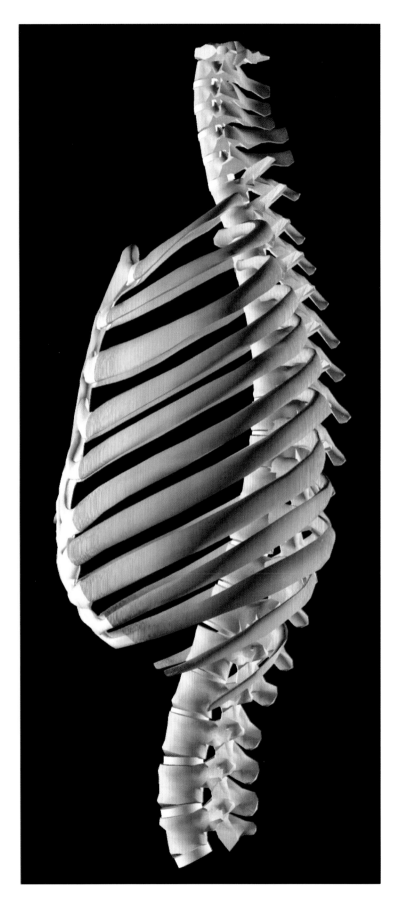

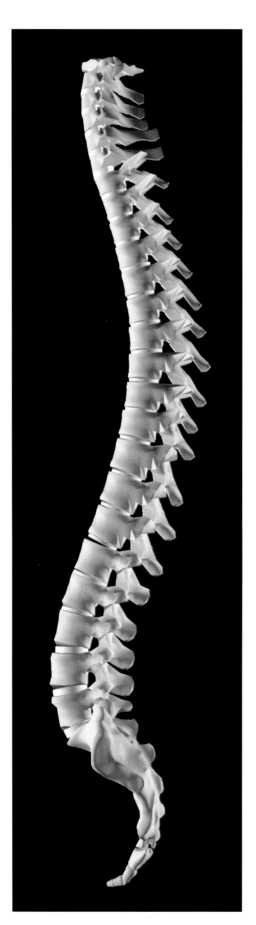

The Spine
The spine comprises thirty-three vertebrae: seven cervical, twelve thoracic, five lumbar, five sacral and four coccygeal.

The Cervical Vertebrae
There are seven vertebrae in this group and of these seven the first and second have special functions. The first is termed the atlas and supports the head: the second is called axis and provides a pivot upon which the atlas and, with it the head, rotate. The remaining five conform with the general pattern of typical vertebrae. A point to note is that the seventh is the first vertebra to possess an undivided spinous process and is noted for its long spine.

The Thoracic Vertebrae
There are twelve vertebrae in this group and they show gradual increase in size from the first to the twelfth. Each vertebra articulates with the ribs which encircle the trunk from the thoracic vertebrae to the sternum in front. Compared with the cervical vertebrae, the thoracic vertebrae are larger.

The Lumbar Vertebrae
There are five lumbar vertebrae in this group, and they can distinguished from the other vertebrae by their greater size. It can be noted that the fifth lumbar vertebra articulates with the sacrum, forming the lumbo-sacral joint.

The Sacrum
There are five vertebrae in this group which are fused together to form a large triangular bone, the sacrum. It is this bone, together with the coccyx, that is wedged between the two innominate bones of the pelvic girdle. The base of the sacrum lies above and articulates with the fifth lumbar vertebra. The sides articulate with the innominate bones and the apex articulates with the coccyx.

The Coccyx
There are four vertebrae in this group, which are fused together to form a small triangular bone articulating above with the sacrum.

Joints of the Skeleton

A sound knowledge of the mechanics of joint function is essential to the understanding of the actions of the muscles.

Joints are formed by the meeting of two of more bones which allow free, slight or no movement at all. Joints may, therefore, be classified as follows:

a) immovable joints

b) slightly movable joints

c) freely movable joints

Immovable Joints

This type of joint is found where the bones are joined by cartilages or by a system of dovetailed edges.

Slightly Movable Joints

Joints of this nature consist of two bony surfaces united by ligaments alone or ligaments with a fibrous cartilage interposed between the bony surfaces.

Freely Movable Joints

In this third class the ends of the bone are covered with cartilage and are connected by a fibrous capsule. The capsule is the synovial membrane which secretes a fluid to lubricate the joint.

Freely movable joints may be classified into six different types:

i)   gliding – whose flat surfaces are capable of only limited movement;

ii) hinge – where the articular surfaces are moulded together to permit movement in one plane only;

iii) pivot – where the movement is limited to rotation;

iv) condyloid – where the articular surface, or condyle, fits into a concave, articular surface, thus allowing flexion, extension, etc;

v)   saddle – the movement here is similar to that of the condyloid, but the surfaces are concavo-convex;

vi) ball and socket – where a spherical head fits into a cup-like cavity and movement is permitted in any direction.

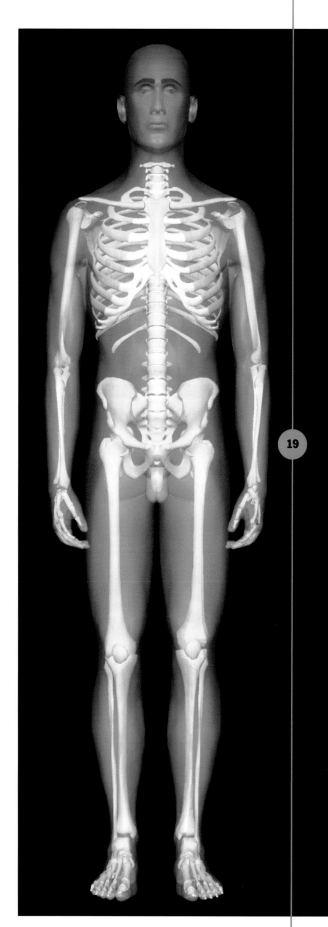

The Detailed Structures of Joints

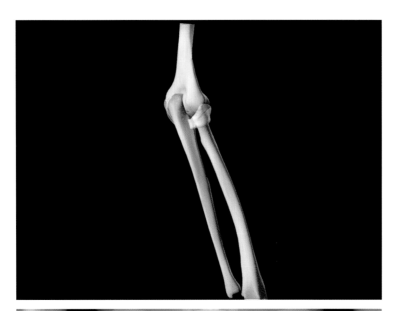

The Elbow Joint

This joint is formed by the articulation of the lower end of the humerus, the upper extremity of the ulna and the head of the radius. The elbow joint is of the hinge type which permits flexion, or bending of the elbow, and extension, or straightening.

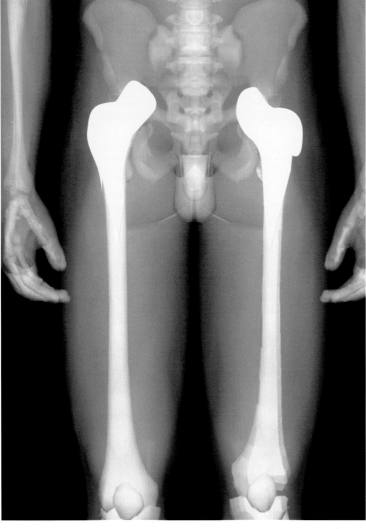

The Hip Joint

The hip joint is of the ball-and-socket type and is formed by the cup-shaped cavity of the acetabulum and the head of the femur. Strong ligaments and a capsule surround the joint. The movements permitted are raising of the thigh (called flexion); bracing the thigh backwards (called extension); raising the thigh sideways, away from the other leg (abduction); moving the thigh from a position of abduction, across the other leg (adduction); rotating the thigh outwards (external rotation); rotating the thigh inwards (internal rotation); circular movement and circumduction.

The Knee Joint

The knee joint is of the hinge type and is formed by the condyles of the femur and the upper end of the tibia. Considering the length of the leg bones, the knee joint may be thought weak, but this is not so, due to the powerful ligaments and muscles around the joint.

The movements at the knee joint are flexion or bending of the knee and extension or straightening of the knee.

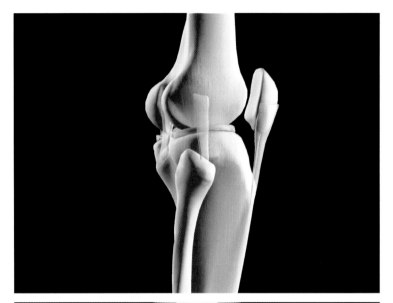

The Shoulder Girdle

The two joints of the shoulder girdle are freely movable gliding joints. The joint between the sternum and the clavicle is the only point at which the shoulder girdle articulates with the trunk, and movement of the clavicle is permitted in all directions. The other joint is where the outer end of the clavicle forms an acromio-clavicular joint with the acromion process of the scapula.

Both these joints are supported by strong ligaments, and movements at the shoulder are: forward rotation; bracing back the shoulders or backward rotation; shrugging the shoulders or elevation; and downward movements of the shoulders or depression.

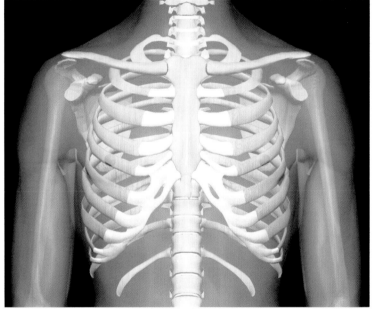

The Ankle Joint

The ankle joint is a hinge-type joint that is formed by the tibia and the
fibula which together form a socket to receive the body of the talus.
Movements of this joint are dorsi-flexion or bending the foot towards the
leg and plantar-flexion or pointing the foot downwards.

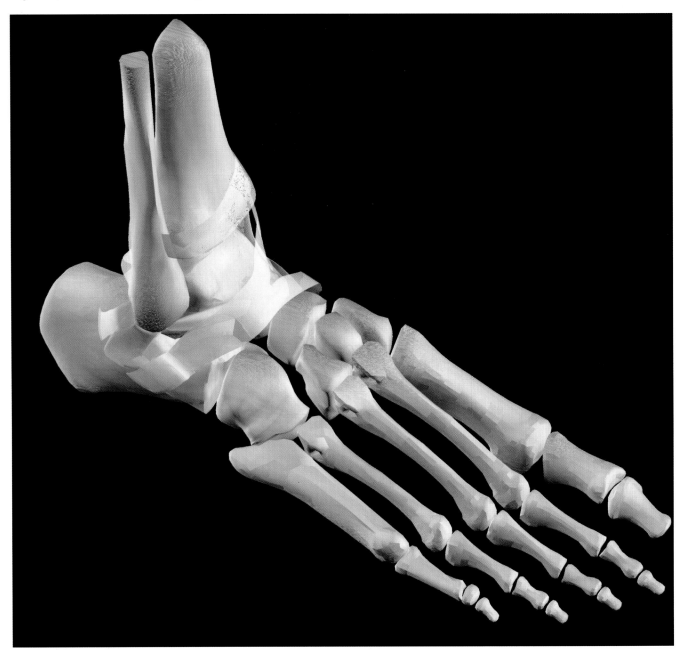

Muscles of the Skeleton

How the Muscles Work

Your muscles cause your body to move by contracting when they are triggered by nerve messages. When skeletal muscles that are attached to bones contract, they pull on the bones and the body moves. Muscles only pull, they cannot push, so for every muscle that causes a movement there is another to undo it. One muscle bends your leg, for example, and another pulls to straighten it. These pairs of muscles are called "antagonists".

The body has three types of muscle that are responsible for all body movement. All muscle types consist of many cells called fibres which contract when stimulated by nerves. However, they differ in several ways: skeletal muscle is attached to bones by strong tendons and causes every kind of voluntary action.

When you want to move, the brain sends an electrical message that is carried to the muscle by nerves. Every single muscle fibre receives the message and contracts simultaneously. This causes the muscle to pull on the bone to which it is attached. In weightlifting terms this is called "the burn".

Smooth muscle forms layers inside organs, and strong cardiac muscle is only found in the heart. The last two types cause involuntary actions.

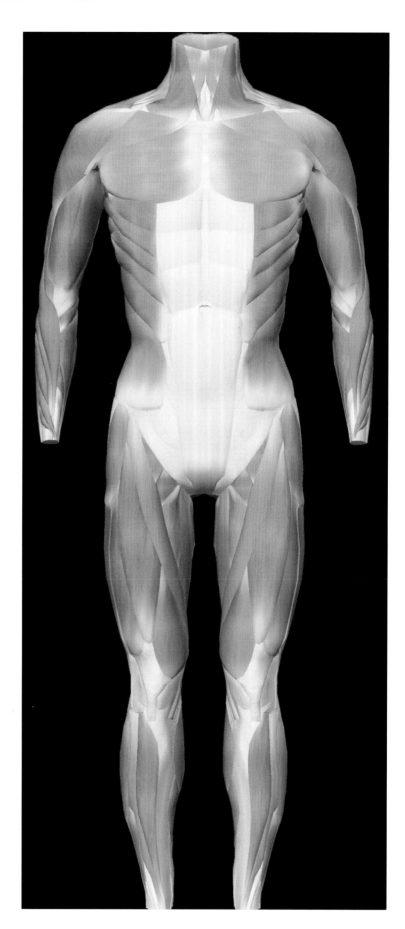

The attention of readers is drawn especially to the fact that this section is to be considered an introduction to this very interesting aspect of human anatomy.

The system employed lists the muscles in chart form. The name, surface position where applicable, attachments and action of the muscles are given.

Attachments

Upper attachments, Lower attachments
- applicable to muscles of the neck and trunk which run more or less vertically
Medial attachments, Lateral attachments
- applicable to muscles which run more or less horizontally
Praximal attachments, Distal attachment
- applicable to muscles of or appertaining to the extremities

Fundamental Movements

The following movements are referred to in the details of the action of a muscle or muscle groups.

Flexion	to reduce the angle at the joint
Extension	to return from flexion
Adduction	to bring towards the mid-line of the body
Elevation	to take away from the mid-line of the body
Depression	to raise, such as lifting the shoulders
Lateral flexion	to pull down, such as pulling down the shoulders
Rotation	rotary movement about the long axis of the bone; this can be inward and outward, and includes supination and pronation of the forearm when flexed at right angles to the upper arm
Circumduction	an orderly circling of a part of the body so that the segment as a whole describes a cone.

The following terms referring to the anatomic position are also used:

Anterior	to the front
Posterior	to the rear
Lateral	to the outside away from the mid-line
Medial	to the inside towards the mid-line
Superior	the top aspect
Inferior	the bottom aspect

A part may be described in a combination of these terms, e.g. anterior/superior or medial/inferior

Principles of Kinetics

Kinesiology is the science of human motion; it selects from relevant sciences those principles that assist in the analysis of physical activity.

Muscle Work

Under this heading a muscle, or muscle group, is considered in the light of whether it shortens, lengthens or holds a fixed position.

Concentric Contraction

In this case the muscle actually shortens against resistance. For example, consider the first part of the two-hands curl. The flexors of the elbow, the brachialis and biceps receive a message from the brain via a motor nerve commanding them to contract. The insertion, being on the forearm bones, is brought towards the origin by the active shortening of those muscles, and they are therefore said to be working concentrically.

Eccentric Contraction

The return from shortening to the muscle's own normal length is called eccentric contraction. It is said to be active lengthening against resistance, but the term lengthening should be used with caution, because as said above, the muscle really returns to its normal length. However, taking the two-hands curl again, consider the second half of the lowering movement. When the weight is lowered from the finishing position, down comes another message telling the same muscles (the elbow flexors) to relax gradually. Gravity pulls the weight towards the ground, and the muscles actively lengthen against the resistance of the weight, until it arrives once more at the starting position. Therefore, the muscles are, in this case, working eccentrically to lower the bar.

Static Contraction

When a muscle is actively engaged in holding a static position, i.e. without changing its length, it is said to be working statically. Thus, if in the two-hands curl the bar was checked halfway through the movement, then the muscles would be working statically to hold the position.

It is now possible to give a generalisation and to say that in barbell and dumbbell exercises the muscles actively engaged in raising the weight work concentrically and in the lowering of the weight they work eccentrically. If the weight were checked in any position, then static contraction would result.

Muscle Action

Closely allied to muscle work is the function of a muscle which contributes to the actual movement, whether it is checking unnecessary movement, or steadying, or stabilising a bone. Under this heading the following terms are used: prime movers; antagonists; synergists; fixators.

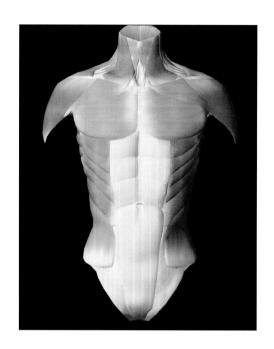

Prime Movers or Agonists

A prime mover is a muscle that is principally responsible for the movement taking place. In most movements there are usually several muscles involved, but basically any movement may be said to have a principal mover and those helping to perform the movement are collectively called the assistant mover.

For example, consider the hold out in front raised. In raising the bar from the thighs the anterior deltoid is the principal mover. In the case of the two-hands curls, the agonists would be the brachialis and biceps, and in the bent-arm pull-over, the triceps.

Antagonists

Basically, an antagonist is a muscle which causes the opposite movement from that of the muscle described under prime movers.

In the two-hands curl it was stated above that the elbow flexors were the prime movers; the muscle which is on the opposite side and has the opposite action is the triceps, so the triceps is the antagonist.

27

Prime Movers and Antagonists

In the two-hands curl the elbow flexors are the prime movers and the triceps are the antagonists, whereas in the bent-arm pull-over the triceps become the prime movers and the elbow flexors become the antagonists.

Synergists

Whilst the term covers several functions, in this context it is intended to imply the basic principle of checking unnecessary movement.

A muscle may cross one or more joints; when it does so, it is capable of movement at every joint it crosses. This, however, is not always desirable and therefore synergic muscle action provides the necessary check.

A classic example is found in the hand. The flexors of the fingers cross many joints including the palm side of the wrist. When an object is picked up or a sponge is squeezed, there is a tendency to flex the wrist as well as the fingers. Therefore, the extensors of the wrist, on the knuckle side, act as a brake, allowing the flexors of the finger to act on the fingers without flexing the wrist. In this example it is the wrist extensors that are acting as synergists.

Fixators

One of the main functions of fixators is the fixing of the origin of the muscles. During the performance of the forward bend rowing motion exercise, the hip extensors (the gluteus maximus, hamstrings and erector spinae) act as fixators in fixing the origin of the latissimus dorsi whilst it works as the prime mover in bringing the arms upwards and backwards to touch the body with the bar.

In the biceps exercise with dumbbells, where the arms are held in the sideways stretch position, the elbows are then bent and straightened while the deltoid holds the upper arms stationary and parallel to the floor. In fixing the origin of the biceps and brachialis the deltoid acts as a fixator.

It will now be seen that, depending on the activity, a single muscle or a muscle group can work concentrically or statically. In short, a muscle may act as a prime mover, an antagonist, a synergist or a fixator.

Range of Movement

Normal, healthy muscles have the ability to work from full extension of a joint to full flexion. This means that they have a full range of movement.

For convenience, the range of movement will be described under the following headings:

a) inner range

b) middle range

c) outer range

Seated dumbell curl

Inner Range

The inner range occurs at the completion of the last third of the movement where the insertion is brought nearest to the attachment of origin, and is, therefore, where the muscle is working at its shortest length.

For examples of this inner range consider the elbow flexors during the near completion of the two-hands curl; the triceps during the completion of the two-hands press or press on back; the quadriceps during the latter few inches of attaining the erect position from the deep knee bend, and so on.

Middle Range

The heading is really self-explanatory: this range is found in the position where the muscle is neither at its shortest nor longest length. In other words, it is passing through the midway position of full range.

The middle range of an exercise usually causes some difficulty, because it is in this range that the function of leverage is unfavourable.

Examples are relatively easy to detect in practice, although the reader is advised not to become confused by bad technique which may lead one to mistake the location of the middle range of an exercise.

Outer Range

It is in this range that the muscle is working at its greatest length in the first third of the movement.

Examples of the outer range are relatively simple, provided the reader has a fair knowledge of the prime movers of the exercise being performed: elbow flexors in the two-hands curl; triceps in the bent-arm pull-over, and so on.

Bench press

There are also certain exercises which do not strictly come under the principle of middle range. However, these movements are not full range. This is because the activity falls short of the full range of movement for a specific exercise.

Once you have grasped the concept of low and high impact exercises, then more advanced development of certain muscle groups can be chosen. If you consider the bench press, even with a heavy weight it is comparatively easy to get the weight moving and the elbows off the floor. This is because the muscles involved are acting as prime movers in their outer range. Once the middle range is reached, the problem of leverage begins to occur, but on reaching the inner range there is little difficulty in locking the elbows.

Training Plans and Programmes

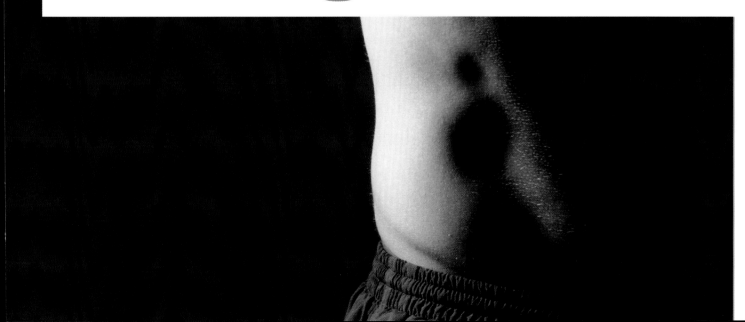

■   ■   ■   ■   ■   ■

It is hoped that this section will help you find the mainstream of the many varied ideas that exist and will show, by careful attention to the build-up of progressive exercise techniques, that success can be achieved and that the overall standard of your lifting can be improved.

In an involvement with any activity it is essential that the participant has a belief system in which he can believe. Such a mind-set must always incorporate the desire to be the best. This quality alone will go a long way in helping to overcome the difficulties and inevitable setbacks that will occur in your lifting career. The lifter must understand the sport thoroughly and all the requirements necessary for success. Such knowledge will help prevent wasting valuable time on unnecessary activity. The term "fitness" must be understood and what it means in relation to the sport; once this knowledge has been taken on board, it must be used with common sense.

It's a true saying that success breeds success, and this remains true at all levels. Even the greatest champions began their weightlifting careers by competing in and winning comparatively minor competitions. These early successes provide the inspiration for further triumphant endeavours. They become the living proof of the lifter's mind-set and provide the strengtheners for their further efforts. Let us consider the mind-set of success in a little more detail.

Fitness for Weightlifting

The first consideration can be posed in the question, "Are you fit enough to be a successful weightlifter?" Even this question contains the qualification of success right from the start. However, before you start you should seek medical advice. Once that minor hurdle has been dealt with you can then proceed with confidence.

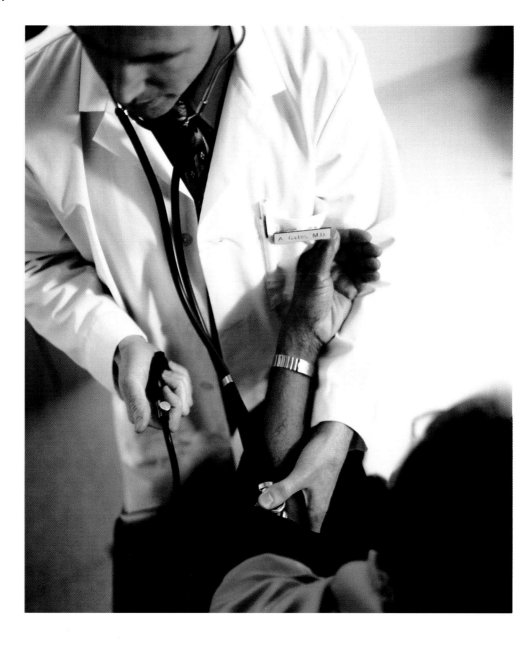

Anyone can lift weights! Many people do so for recreational purposes alone and one must not decry the pleasure that they derive from such participation. In our context, however, success applies to winning – to pushing oneself to the limits of personal ability. What, then, is our special fitness? It is the ability to perform the activity of weightlifting with success and to be able to recover quickly. Let's see how this definition can be applied to the sport and the essential steps necessary to make it viable.

Strength

It is vital to develop great strength. This is what the basis of weightlifting is all about. No weak lifters are champions. Fortunately, this is perhaps the easiest aspect of the activity and in the sport the sky is the limit as far as building up strength is concerned. Most successful weightlifters are much stronger than their technical ability will permit them to show.

Speed

The quality of speed is the ultimate end product of all the major athletic events that are not specifically judged on an aesthetic presentation. Weightlifting is a fast, explosive activity. Maximum force needs to be generated in the shortest possible time. This means that the faster you can bring great strength you have developed into effective play, the greater and more impressive your power will be.

Power

In weightlifting terms power is force (strength) multiplied by velocity (speed). Power is the most important factor in the successful accomplishment of all weightlifting and other athletic events of a fast, explosive nature. Combined with physical strength, the quality of speed can be developed and at certain times in your training schedule and this should be given special attention.

Fitness

In preparing a plan and corresponding schedule of work, it is too easy for the lifter to get carried away by unrealistically ambitious ideas of workouts. As time passes he will find that he is incapable of completing. The reason why he will be unable to fulfil his best intentions will be his lack of fitness for the weight-load that he has set himself.

Actual physical fitness is difficult to define, because it varies considerably from activity to activity. The sprint runner could not be expected to lift the heavy weights handled by the lifter, or the lifter to run the sprint, so the fitness requirements will be seen to be different in each case. In our original definition we talk of being able to recover quickly. This means: having undertaken to train at a certain load level, it is essential that the lifter can recover quickly enough to be able to repeat his training at a similar or greater load at subsequent training sessions on alternate days. Often the best-laid plans fail because the lifter finds that he cannot recover quickly enough from one workout to another. Remember, never sacrifice poundage for technique.

Strength is developed by resistance to overload. General physical fitness is achieved by your body's physical exhaustion. To put this simply means that the systems of the body, which involve heart, lungs and circulation, are stimulated to greater efficiency by subjecting them to levels of work over and above those normally necessary for the ordinary living process.

In books on physical fitness these physical systems are referred to as cardiovascular (heart and circulation) and respiratory (efficient use of oxygen and expiration of carbon dioxide). Since much weightlifting training (training for power) necessitates the use of heavy weights and, consequently, low repetitions, placing heavy overload on the muscular system only, little is done to develop cardiovascular and respiratory fitness. An intensive workout is essential to build up upper body strength and overall fitness. It is a very good idea to rest for a day after a full workout to give your body's systems a chance to repair and build important musculature. Remember that rest is as important to your body as weight training itself.

In physiological terms much of the training for weightlifting is of an anaerobic nature (muscle work without direct oxygen supply from breathing), but for maximum efficiency work of an aerobic type (with direct oxygen supply from breathing) is also needed.

Using a Trainer or Workout Partner

In the training of the sport a great deal of attention is always paid to the mastery of the lifts, and a sound understanding of the principles of your workout is essential. In weightlifting the movements of the two lifts are difficult and unusual, and it is especially important to remember that they are to be applied to a "changing apparatus". (By this is meant that there is a considerable difference between a first attempt clean

and jerk, with a weight that should be overcome comparatively easily, and a third attempt which may well be a personal or even a national or world record. The apparatus has effectively been changed. This change can disturb a lifter's mind-set and enthusiasm and could possibly cause your technique to break down. The activity of weightlifting is therefore complex psychologically as well as physically. The thinking process and ability to concentrate is as vital as physical strength. It is never a good idea to allow your mind to wander when attempting to perform an exercise.

Your training routine must always include work related to the maintenance and development of correct muscles. Your build-up techniques must be basically consistent, always remembering to rest the muscle group that you have exercised for 24 hours before working it again. This will give the muscle a chance to repair and rebuild itself so it can take on the task of bearing a heavy weight load again.

Your schedule should be reinforced constantly by correct practice of the lifts. At the extreme range of physical stress, such as in a competitive field, skill must not let the competitor down.

Flexibility is essential in the mastery of training technique and thereby the full exploitation of the other qualities for which weightlifters workout. Involved with the training is the necessity for a full range of mobility in all body movements.

Motivation and Goals

We all want to be the best at what we do! This ambitious desire can be reinforced by many forms of motivational methods. Motivation can be achieved through external rewards, such as money, houses, cars, improved job and family prospects and so on, but since such are unlikely to come the way of weightlifting, the motivating factors that make the competitor must come from within. It is too easy to lose heart or if one's mind-set is not on the job at hand. Without the right positive mental attitude, a training schedule is unlikely to succeed, so building up the mental muscles are every bit as important as building up the physical ones. The key to success is self-belief and personal discipline.

Determination and single-mindedness of purpose are the cornerstones of the strength of character that is needed by a successful weightlifter. He must be prepared to work very hard and to overcome the relatively minor setbacks of occasional failure. Most people who achieve greatness have an innate advantage, but it is only by using their natural talents to the full and by working very hard that they reach the top of their chosen field of activity.

Sporting activity is a natural part of man's development. Our species is always striving to conquer, to establish himself as the prime living creature. Much progress in the history of mankind has been dependent upon his intelligence and search for knowledge. Man's development in weightlifting, as in other sporting fields, depends upon the removal of inhibitions. This is achieved by repeatedly submitting oneself to suitable stressful situations within the training context and by overcoming them successfully. These conditions exist in both training and your personal gains. The training plan and schedules must be arranged to fit into your lifestyle with minimum hindrance while always allowing you to train on your chosen days. They must be designed to overcome stressful situations and not to create conflict or stress from outside interference or through a too hasty attempt at physical advancement.

Summary

Our philosophy can be expressed, therefore, in the need for:

1 the development of great strength

2 the development of speed and athletic ability

3 the development, as a consequence of 1 and 2, of great power

4 the development of systematic fitness and physical hardness

5 the mastery of technique

6 the desire to be the best, reinforced by motivating factors

Thought and Movement

The technique of weightlifting is based on the science of simple and natural movement. The objective is to exert maximum force in the most efficient manner. To achieve this you should concentrate particularly on –

1   Natural body balance

2   The economical use of effort

Once you have achieved control in these two areas then you will be able to use both your natural strength and effort to develop the maximum force you will need to build up, and overcome, the task of lifting the barbell.

The prospective lifter must develop the necessary strength and determination to overcome a heavy weight. May exercises many seem to be unnatural but this is not the case. The pull, especially, is difficult for a beginner to master.

There is a potential problem in that those movements which seem to be natural, such as leaning one's body weight against the resistance can LEAD TO SERIOUS INJURY THAT CANNOT BE CORRECTED. This cannot be emphasised enough. It is ESSENTIAL that the correct technique should be understood and used from the very start of a weightlifter's career.

The experienced weightlifter can also fall into bad habits when he is handling extremely heavy weights. THE CORRECT TECHNIQUE SHOULD NOT BE SACRIFICED TO THE DESIRE TO TACKLE HEAVIER WEIGHTS.

Bad habits, once formed, are often impossible to break. Even when basic faults may appear to have been eradicated there is always the danger that under pressure and stress, a return to the initial learned fault is all too easy even after a period of extensive training.

At the risk of repeating myself, the two vital areas of technique in any athletic exercise are natural body balance and the economical use of effort.

Correct Body Balance

Body balance is a state of control and stability, without giving in to a strong tendency to move out of balance. To lose your natural body balance is to lose control. The physical mechanics of this are very simple and related to adopting the correct posture as in the example of the basic barbell lift or cross/snatch.

Economical Use of Effort

The economical use of effort is a neat phrase but what actually does it mean to the beginner? If you have been weight training for some time you probably won't find it necessary to start with the beginner programme. Economy of effort is a system of action designed so that you can see some fast, early improvements in your physique and strength capacity which you can fine-tune at a later date.

It may be that you regard yourself as a novice and think that a beginner programme is for you. After you have started a regime of weightlifting you may then find that it seems too easy. In which case, you should move on to the next stage immediately by increasing your poundage and effort until you find that you have again reached a plateau in your personal fitness development. When this occurs you can remain at this level for a period of recuperation enabling you to move on again when you feel yourself ready for the challenge.

If, however you have been pumping iron for some time, the initial routine may seem tedious, stale and very, very familiar.

The basic principle at work here is that of the lever. A lever operates on the principle of the fulcrum that provides the leverage. In weightlifting the long bones and spine are the levers, the power points are where the muscles are attached to the bones at the joints. These are the fulcrums. It is vital to remember that in weightlifting the fulcrums must always be moved towards the resistance.

The Three Stages of Resistance

Weightlifting is about resistance. Simply having a weight that is too light or so heavy that you can't lift it off the bench is not going to get you anywhere at all. First of all you must find the weight that is suitable for your body type and strength. Not too light nor too heavy. You must be able to perform a minimum of five repetitions of a specific exercise and be able hold it at the failure point for several seconds and lower or raise that specific weight. Personal experimentation is the key to success in this area.

1 Starting Position – The Pull
2 The Holding Position
3 The Lowering Position

Both the Starting Position or Pull and the Lowering Position are dynamic in the sense that the former requires great power to overcome the inertia of the bar and to develop acceleration, while the latter demands great control in a lowering position. The mastery of both require a great deal of skill and, therefore, considerable time should be spent in mastering the techniques of these movements.

The Holding Position part of the lift refers to the actual transition from pulling to the lowering position. At this time the centre of gravity of your body is transferred to wherever the weight you are training with is. The lower body may seem weightless as the feet have a tendency to leave the ground. Therefore at this time you can have little or no control over the shake of the feet or the direction of the sway. This is very dangerous because your body is losing its centre of gravity and you will find yourself rapidly losing control of the bar.

The position through which the lifter goes will be controlled very much by the technique, satisfactory or otherwise, that has been adopted in the pull and this will consequently affect the lowering position. Although mistakes may become obvious in the holding position, their origin will probably be in an error made at some stage of the pull (usually right at the very start). It is easy to see, for instance, that a lifter has dropped the bar behind the head in the squat snatch. At this point, any worthwhile trainer should be observing carefully to see where the basic error originated, and must be able to give positive advice to eliminate the mistake at the source.

The Key Positions are:

1   Starting Position – this refers to the exact moment when the bar leaves the platform

2   Bar at knee height

3   Full extension at the top of the pull

4   Receiving Position

The following section is very important indeed. It should be studied carefully, especially those areas that are designated "Key Positions".

Your trainer will ensure that you are passing through these positions at all stages of the lift.

If you fail to pass through these positions properly the cause is likely to be any of the following reasons:
1 Lack of strength in any of the essential muscle groups working at any stage of the lift
2 Loss of balance
3 Use of the wrong muscle groups at the wrong time, in other words: the lack of co-ordinated muscular effort
4 Lack of full joint mobility
5 Inability to develop speed as a result of weight

These notes apply to all the basic starting positions for all the exercises described in this book. Please apply the following directions to all exercises, but remember that adjustments are possible regarding the width of grip for the snatch.

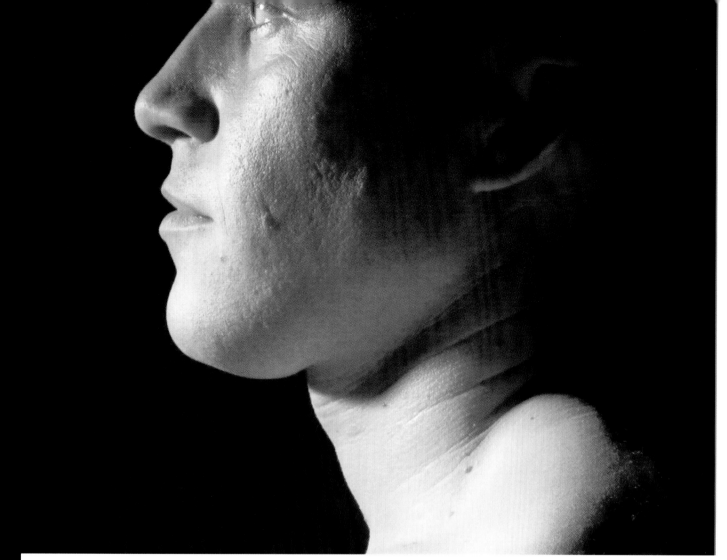

The Exercises

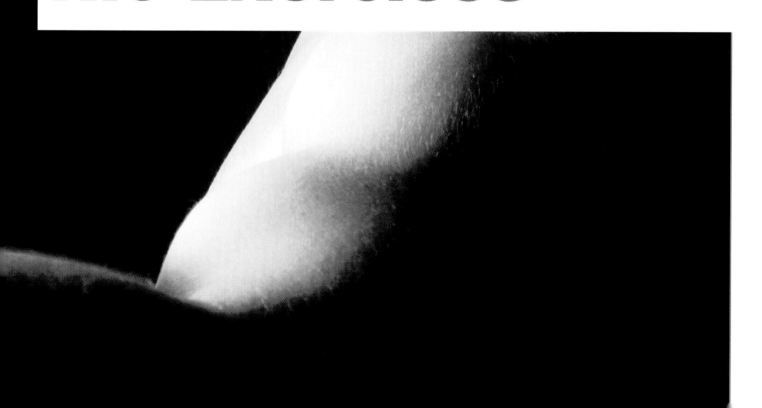

The Exercises

Starting Position (Key Position No 1)

Feet	Approximately hip-width apart, toes turned out slightly. Feel the weight of the body over the whole of the foot. This will ensure good balance.
Knees	The angle at the knees should be slightly bent (between 90-100 degrees).
Back	The back should be slightly in front of the bar.
Shoulders	The shoulders should be slightly in front of the bar.
Arms	The arms should be straight, but not locked rigid. This is described as being athletically straight.
Elbows	The elbows should be turned out from the side of the body. This will ensure a more vertical pull.
Grip	Clean and jerk. Basically, the grip for this lift will be just slightly wider than shoulder width.
Snatch	The width of grip is decided by measuring the distance from elbow joint to elbow joint across the back when the arms are raised horizontally. This distance is then marked on the bar. The hands should be spaced accordingly so that the marks lie between the first and second fingers.

Points in Common for Both Lifts

It is essential that you work with a trainer when you begin this movement because injury may result from bad posture.

The hook grip should be used for all attempts. The head should be tilted closer to the vertical than the angle of the back. Look directly forward.

First stage of the lift movement of bar from Key Position No 1 (starting position) to Key Position No 2 (bar at knee height).

Due to the forward inclination of the shin bone in the starting position, the barbell is positioned over the front part of the foot. This is incorrect because you are leaning too far forward for a correct lift. If the bar were to be lifted in a vertical line, you would be physically pulled forwards to the front of your toes and consequently off balance.

The barbell must be eased back and into the shins as it is lifted from the floor so that by the time it is at knee height (Key Position No 2) it is directly over the centre of your stance. This position ensures that you will be in balance at a vital part of the lift and will consequently be able to exert maximum force as you pass through this area of greatest resistance.

This is the only deliberate movement of the bar out of a vertical line of lift. Your trainer should teach you this movement from the start of your training programme.

Floor Exercises

Exercise 1: push-up

The push-up is a classic exercise for strengthening the wrists, shoulders and upper back.

A Lie facing the floor with your hands either side of your head, palms down and shoulder-width apart. Balance your weight on the balls of your feet and the palms of your hands. Extend your arms fully, but don't lock the elbows. Your legs should be together and fully extended; your fingers should point forwards. Make sure that your legs, back and neck form a straight line. Keep your eyes on the floor.

B Keeping your body straight, bend your arms slowly, and lower yourself until your chest almost touches the floor. Hold the position for one second before returning slowly to the starting position.

47

Additional Sequence

Exercise 2: decline push-up

Decline push-ups are a more taxing variation of the classic exercise.

A Start as for Exercise 1, with your legs together and arms extended (see page 47). Instead of having your feet on the ground, rest them on a weight bench. Your elbows should be slightly bent; your fingers should point forwards. Make sure that your legs, back and neck form a straight line. Keep your eyes on the floor.

B Keeping your body straight, bend your arms slowly, and lower yourself until your chest almost touches the floor. Hold the position for one second before returning slowly to the starting position.

Exercise 3: hip raises

This exercise works all the major muscle groups in your torso as well as the bottom and thigh muscle groups. It is particularly good as an all-round build up.

A Lie flat on the floor facing the ceiling, with your arms by your sides, palms down. Without locking your knees, and keeping your toes pointed, raise your legs in the air.

B Hold in your abdominals and slowly lift your hips off the floor, shifting your weight towards your shoulders Make sure you keep your legs vertical. Hold the position for a few seconds and then slowly return to the starting position.

Exercise 4: negative sit-ups with weight plates

This is an excellent exercise for building the upper and lower abdominals.

A   Sit on the floor holding a suitable weight plate to your chest. Bend your knees and, keeping your feet flat on the ground a shoulder-width apart, tuck them under a suitably secure object. You can buy special items of equipment for this purpose, but a weights bench or sofa, will also do. Alternatively, your training partner could hold your feet.

B   Holding the weight plate firmly in place, slowly lower your torso until your back almost touches the floor. *Never* go all of the way down. Hold the position for a few seconds and then slowly raise yourself up again.

Repeat the exercise.

49

Exercise 5: curl-up with weight plates

Another great exercise for building the major abdominal muscles.

A   Lie flat on your back holding a suitable weight plate to your chest and your elbows pointing outwards. With your knees bent at an angle of approximately 45°, place your feet a shoulder-width apart under a suitably heavy object, such as a weights bench or sofa.

B   To a count of two, and holding the weight plate firmly to your chest, raise your torso up, towards your knees, lifting your shoulder blades as far off the ground as you can. Keep your knees in line with your feet. Count to two again before returning slowly to the starting position.

Exercise 6: side bends (no weight)

With this exercise, it is important to keep your body perfectly rigid and facing forward. Never twist your torso to the side, because there is a danger of pulling the muscles in your back. This exercise is essential for upper body movement.

A Stand upright with your arms hanging by your sides, the palms facing inwards. Position your feet a shoulder-width apart.

B Bend to one side slowly, tensing the lateral-oblique muscles until you feel the stretch. Return to the starting position, slowly, and then repeat the movement.

C Complete a set on one side of your body before repeating the exercise on the opposite side.

Exercise 7: curl-up

This exercise targets the upper and lower abdominal wall.

A Lie flat on your back with your hands cupped behind your head and your elbows pointing outwards. With your knees bent at an angle of approximately 45°, place your feet a shoulder-width apart under a suitably heavy object, such as a weights bench or sofa.

B Keeping your hands in position, raise your torso up, towards your knees, lifting your shoulder blades as far off the ground as you can, and contracting your abdominal muscles as you go. Keep your knees in line with your feet. Do not use your hands to curl or pull your neck, as this will put pressure on your spine. Hold the position for a second, before returning, slowly to the starting position.

Finish the set without resting between repetitions.

Exercise 8: oblique trunk rotation

Concentrate on performing this exercise in one slow, continuous motion.

A Lie on your back with your knees bent and your feet tucked under a support, such as the base of a weights machine or bench. This will stabilise your lower body.

B Holding your torso at an angle of 45° to the floor, start the exercise by moving your torso slowly to the left.

C Keep to the left as you lower yourself down, onto your back. Then move to the right as you start to raise your torso again.

D Move continuously through each clockwise rotation.

Now repeat the exercise, this time moving down on your right side and around to your left.

Exercise 9: close-grip chin-up

A chin bar is necessary for this exercise, which works the arms and shoulders. There is also a wide-grip variation, which involves different positioning for the hands.

A Grasp a handle suspended from the chin bar. Use both hands, palms facing the same way. You should hang about 15cm (6in) above the floor when your arms are fully extended. Keep your knees slightly bent.

B Using your lateral muscles and not the biceps, pu yourself up slowly, until your torso almost touche your hands. Lower yourself down again slowly.

Exercise 10: standing kick-back

This exercise also tones your hamstrings.

A Fasten an ankle weight around your right ankle. Stand facing a wall, gently holding on to it with your hands to help you to balance. Lean forward slightly, so that your whole body forms a straight line. Now shift your weight onto your left leg.

B Slowly raise your right leg as far behind you as you can, feeling the contraction in your bottom. Your knee should be slightly bent, but don't arch your back or overextend yourself. Hold the position for a second, then slowly lower your leg.

Exercise 11: kneeling kick-back

This exercise can be performed with or without ankle weights. The movement will also help to improve hip flexibility.

A You have the option of fixing ankle weights around both ankles to give additional resistance for this movement. Get down on your hands and knees.

B Slowly raise your left leg behind you until your thigh is parallel with your torso. Keep the left knee slightly bent. Hold this position for a second, then return slowly to the starting position. Just as you get there, raise your right leg again before it touches the floor.

Finish the set, then switch legs and repeat the exercise.

53

Exercise 12: bent-kick cross

You may find this exercise strange, but it is great for targetting and building butt muscles.

A To start the exercise, get down on your hands and knees and raise your left knee a few inches off the floor.

B Push the left leg up and back behind you, forcing your heel towards the ceiling, and contracting your gluteal muscles as you push upwards. Hold this position for a second, then slowly lower your leg to the starting position.

Finish the set, then switch to your right leg and repeat the exercise.

Exercise 13: standing back-leg swing

This exercise works the muscles at the back of the thigh and of the bottom. This dynamic move also greatly increases the range of movement of the legs, and loosens and strengthens the front of the hips and thighs.

A Stand with your right side against a ballet warm-up bar or an exercise machine, and hold on to it with your right hand.

B Supporting your weight on your right leg, raise your left leg as high as possible in front of you. Keep your left leg slightly bent. Hold the position for a second.

C Let your left leg fall and swing a far behind your body as it will comfortably go. Hold this position for a second, then retur to the starting position.

Finish the set, then switch to your right side and repeat the exercise.

Exercise 14: single-leg squat

This exercises the gluteal muscles as well as the back and hips.

A Place a sturdy chair or piece of exercise equipment to your right. You are going to rest your right hand on it for balance. Stand in an upright position, with your feet a shoulder-width apart and your knees slightly bent. Your back should be straight.

B Slowly bend your right knee while extending your left leg out in front of you. Once your right thigh is parallel with the floor, slowly raise yourself back up into the starting position. Don't pause between repetitions – you should look like a piston pumping up and down – and make sure you keep your back straight throughout the exercise.

Finish the set, then switch legs and repeat the exercise.

Exercise 15: Calf raises

You will need some kind of step or platform for this exercise – a large book, say, 5 to 8cm (2 to 3in) thick would be suitable.

A Step on to the platform, so that just the balls of your feet and toes rest on it and your heels are suspended over the edge.

B Slowly raise your body, lifting your heels until you feel your calf muscles pulling. Hold this position for one second before lowering yourself to the starting position.

Begin with ten repetitions of this move, slowly building up the number of repetitions as your weight-training regime progresses.

dumbbell exercises

Exercise 1: front-deltoid raises

Use this exercise to work the upper-arm muscles – the trapezius and the pectorals – as well as the shoulders.

To start with, keep the dumbbell low in weight. Furthermore, you should take this exercise gradually, building up your strength over a period of time.

A Stand with your feet a shoulder-width apart and your knees slightly bent. Take a dumbbell in each hand and let your arms hang down by your sides. Your elbows should be slightly bent and your palms should face inwards. Keeping your lower back straight, lean forward *very slightly* at the waist, with your elbows back and your chest pushed out.

B Now raise your left arm in front of you, slowly, until it is level with your shoulder, and your palm is facing the floor. *Do not* rock your hips or swing your arms to gain momentum. Hold the position for a few seconds, before slowly returning to the starting position.

C Complete one set with the left arm and then repeat the exercise with the right arm.

Exercise 2: bent-over lateral raise

This exercise can be used to work the back deltoid muscles.

A Take a dumbbell in each hand and bend forward at the waist. Your arms should be in front of you with the elbows slightly bent, and palms facing each other. Keep your feet a little more than shoulder-width apart. *Always* keep your back straight and roughly parallel to the floor.

B Raise both dumbbells at the same time, slowly, pushing them out to the side. Keep going until your arms are parallel to the floor. Keep your back straight. Hold the position for a few seconds before returning slowly to the starting position.

Exercise 3: shrugs

This exercise can be used to strengthen your rhomboids – which lie between your spine and the shoulder blades – and to develop your shoulders.

A Stand up straight, with your feet a shoulder-width apart and your knees slightly bent. Take a dumbbell in each hand and let your arms hang down by your sides. Your palms should be facing inwards and your shoulders should be held back and relaxed.

B Keep your head still and your chin tucked in slightly as you slowly shrug your shoulders as high as they will go. Hold the position for one second before slowly returning to the starting position.

Exercise 4: side-deltoid raise

This exercise can be used to work your side deltoids.

A Stand with your feet a shoulder-width apart and your knees slightly bent. Take a dumbbell in each hand and let your arms hang down by your sides. Your elbows should be slightly bent and your palms should face inwards. Your shoulders should be relaxed, your chest should be extended and your lower back straight, but with a slight lean.

B Raising both dumbbells at the same time, lift you arms out to the sides until they are level with your shoulders. Keep your elbows slightly bent, and make sure your arms stay in the same plane as your torso. Hold the position for one second before slowly lowering your arms to the starting position.

Exercise 5: hammer curl

Use this exercise to target the elbow flexor muscles and your biceps.

A Stand with your feet a shoulder-width apart and your knees slightly bent. Take a dumbbell in each hand and let your arms hang down by your sides. Your elbows should be slightly bent and your palms should face inwards.

B Slowly curl the left dumbbell until the end touches your shoulder. *Do not* rotate your wrist, but *do* keep your upper arm and elbow stationary. Hold the position for one second before lowering the dumbbell slowly to the starting position. Make the motion in one controlled sweep.

Slowly repeat the exercise with the right dumbbell.

Exercise 6: alternating dumbbell curl

Another exercise for the elbow flexors.

A Stand with your feet a shoulder-width apart and your knees slightly bent. Take a dumbbell in each hand and let your arms hang down by your sides. Your elbows should be slightly bent and your palms should face inwards.

B Now curl the left dumbbell slowly, up towards your collarbone. As you do so, rotate the arm slightly so that your palm now faces up. Hold the position for one second before lowering the dumbbell slowly, in one controlled sweep. Repeat the exercise with your left arm.

Exercise 7: side bends with dumbbells

This exercise, for strengthening side-to-side movement, is suited to the more advanced weight-trainer,

using free weights to provide more resistance while performing the set.

A Stand upright with your feet a shoulder-width apart and your knees slightly bent. Take a dumbbell in each hand and let your arms hang down by your sides with your palms facing inwards.

B Bend to one side, slowly, allowing the dumbbell to drop down until you feel your lateral obliques pulling. Keep your body in the same plane, facing outwards and *do not* move your torso into a twist or rock from side to side. Once you have gone as low as you can, slowly bring yourself back up to the starting position, keeping your abdominal muscles and lateral obliques contracted.

Finish the set without resting between repetitions and then repeat the set for the opposite side.

Exercise 8: toe touch

Use this exercise to work your gluteal muscles and hamstrings.

A   Stand with your feet a
   shoulder-width apart and your
   knees unlocked. Take a
   dumbbell in your left hand.

B   Bend forwards and to the right,
   slowly, and touch the
   dumbbell against your right
   foot. Hold the position for one
   second before returning slowly
   to the starting position

Exercise 9: dumbbell swing

This exercise is great for
strengthening your lower
back, but also
strengthens the
hamstrings, deltoids and
glutes. It should be
performed using an
explosive movement.

Caution
Start by using very
light weights and
performing high
repetitions.

A   Stand with your feet slightly more
   than a shoulder-width apart and your
   knees unlocked. Take a dumbbell in
   both hands and bend forward at the
   waist until the dumbbell is between
   your shins. Your arms should be fully
   extended and your back straight.
   (Keep the weight off the floor.)

B   Now swing the dumbbell up over
   your head, making sure you stay
   upright, with your back held straight.
   Hold the dumbbell over your head
   for one second, then bend at the
   waist as you return to the starting
   position.

64

Exercise 10: alternating lunge

This movement works the quadriceps. It is a dynamic movement, building strength and coordination.

A Stand with your feet a shoulder-width apart and a dumbbell in each hand. Your upper body should be upright, with your head in line with your spine.

B Step forward with your left leg, planting the foot firmly on the floor and bending your knees until your right shin is parallel with the floor. Your left knee should not extend past the end of your left foot. Your right leg should be extended behind you, with the knee slightly bent and the heel raised. Bring your left left back into the starting position, pressing your right heel into the ground. Your feet should be a shoulder-width apart.

Repeat the exercise using your right leg. That makes one repetition.

Barbell Exercises

Exercise 1: behind-the-neck press with barbell

This is an all-purpose exercise, working the back deltoids, pectorals, upper-back triceps and ribcage muscles. It can also be performed at the front of the neck (see Exercise 2: overhead press with barbell, see opposite). If you like, you can alternate between the two. It is a good idea to use lighter weights than usual for this exercise, in accordance with the rule of gradually building up your resistance to the weight.

A Sit on a bench with your back straight and your feet a shoulder-width apart. Hold a barbell behind your neck, across the top of your shoulders. Position your hands so that they are slightly more than a shoulder-width apart, palms facing forwards. Keep your elbows pointed downwards and your chest extended. *Do not arch your back!*

B Making sure you keep your elbows pointing outwards, slowly raise the barbell straight upwards. Pull your head forward slightly as you do so. Hold the position for one second before slowly lowering the barbell to the starting position.

66

Exercise 2: overhead press with barbell

Use this exercise to work the front and side deltoids. You can alternate the

movement with Exercise 1: behind-the-neck press with barbell (see opposite).

A Sit on a bench with your back straight and your feet a shoulder-width apart. Hold the barbell overhand, with your hands at least a shoulder-width apart. Bend your elbows and raise the barbell until it is level with your shoulders. Keep your elbows pointing downwards and your chest extended.

B Now lift the barbell slowly, straight over your head. Hold the position for one second before slowly lowering the barbell to chest level again.

Now repeat the exercise.

Exercise 3: upright rowing

This exercise is excellent for strengthening your biceps and forearms, and for developing your shoulders.

A Standing upright, take a barbell in both hands using a narrow grip. Keep your palms facing downwards. Your arms should be fully extended in front of you, and the barbell should be level with your upper thighs. Relax your shoulders slightly and keep your back straight.

B Lift the barbell, slowly, straight over your head and hold the position for one second before slowly lowering the barbell to chest level again.

Now repeat the exercise.

You can also do the exercise using a wide grip.

68

Exercise 4: barbell curl

This exercise works the elbow flexors.

A Stand straight, with your knees slightly bent. Hold a barbell with your hands a shoulder-width apart, the palms facing upwards. Your arms should be extended in front of you, with the barbell at thigh level.

B With your elbows held close to your body, use the biceps to curl the barbell up slowly towards your chin. Keep your wrists straight throughout the curl and *do not* sway your back or rock your body to gain momentum. Hold the position for one second before returning slowly to the starting position. Always use a smooth, controlled motion.

Exercise 5: reverse-grip barbell curl

Use this exercise to work the flexor muscles at the front of the arms.

A Stand straight, with your knees slightly bent. Hold a barbell with your hands a shoulder-width apart, the palms facing upwards. Your arms should be extended in front of you, with the barbell at thigh level, and your elbows should be well tucked in.

B Curl the barbell towards your chin, slowly, and hold the position for one second at the end of the lift. Then slowly lower the barbell to the starting position, using a smooth, controlled action.

Exercise 6: Romanian dead-lift

This is an all-purpose exercise for strengthening the back, arms, shoulders and legs.

Caution
Use less weight than you would for a normal dead-lift (see page 71).

A Take a lightly weighted barbell in both hands. They should be a shoulder-width apart, with one palm facing outwards and the other facing in. Hold the barbell at mid-thigh level, with your arms fully extended, your back straight, your shoulders back and your chest pushed out. Pause for a second.

B Now bend forward at the hips, slowly, keeping the barbell close to your thighs. Keep your back straight and bend your knees slightly. Gradually lower the barbell towards the floor as far as you can comfortably go. Make the movement slow and controlled as you return to the starting position, remembering to keep your back straight as you go.

Exercise 7: wide-grip row

A versatile movement that works the back deltoids, bottom and abs.

A Stand upright with your feet a shoulder-width apart and your knees slightly bent. Bend forward at the waist until your upper body is parallel with the floor. Do not arch your back, Take a barbell in a grip wider than shoulder-width and with your palms facing the body.

B To a count of two, raise the barbell up until it touches your chest. Your elbows should be higher than your back. Hold the position for one second before slowly lowering the barbell level with the middle of your shins.

Repeat the exercise.

Exercise 8: dead-lift

A versatile movement that strengthens your legs, shoulders and arms.

A Stand up straight, with a lightly weighted barbell on the floor before you. Bend over the barbell and grasp it with your hands, which should be a shoulder-width apart, with one palm facing inwards and the other out. Keep your back is straight and your arms and legs stiff and fairly straight. Do not lock the elbows or knees.

B Slowly lift the barbell until it is level with your upper-thigh. Your back, arms and legs should remain straight and your knees should not be locked. Hold the position for one second, before slowly lowering the weight again.

Exercise 9: good morning

Use this move to strengthen your lower back, and to work the hamstrings, abs and gluteals. It is not recommended for beginners. To avoid injury, use an empty bar at first, and pay close attention to your form. You can move on to light weights when you have mastered the movement.

A Stand up straight with your legs a shoulder-width apart, and do not lock your knees. Hold a barbell across your shoulders. Your hands should be slightly more than shoulder-width apart, palms facing outwards. Lean forward slightly at the waist, keeping your upper body straight, your shoulders back and your chest pushed out.

B Keeping your back straight, bend over slowly at the waist, until your upper body is parallel with the floor. Keep your eyes looking forward, not down. Hold the position for one second, before slowly returning to the starting position.

Exercise 10: hack squat

The hack squat puts less pressure on your knees and lower back than the normal squat, but it does require greater balancing skills.

Caution

To avoid injury, start with an unweighted barbell, then slowly add more weight as you master the movement. (You should still use less weight than you would for a normal squat.)

A Stand with your feet shoulder-width apart, and a barbell positioned directly behind you. Squat down, gripping the bar with both hands, palms facing away from your body. Your hands should be slightly more than a shoulder-width apart. Stand up, keeping the bar at arm's length behind your thighs. Be sure to keep your head in line with your body.

B Squat down slowly, until your thighs are almost parallel with the floor. Your knees should not extend beyond your toes. Hold the position for one second, before rising slowly again. Keep your arms fully extended.

Exercise 11: lateral squat

This exercise targets the gluteal muscles and the sides of your thighs. Use dumbbells instead of a barbell if you are a beginner.

A Stand upright, with a barbell positioned evenly across your upper back and shoulders. The grip should be as wide as you can make it, with your palms facing away from the body. Place your feet in a wide stance, toes pointing outwards, and your head in line with your body.

B Keeping your right leg straight, slowly lean to the left, so that you drop down until your left thigh is parallel with the floor. Don't let your knee turn inwards or extend beyond your toes. Most of your weight should be on your right leg, while your left leg should extended and slightly bent at the knee. Hold the stance for one second before returning to the starting position again by slowly extending your left leg and bringing your torso back to the centre.

Without resting, repeat the exercise using your left leg. That makes one repetition.

Exercise 12: drop squat

This great all-purpose exercise conditions large muscle groups (specifically your thighs and gluteal muscles), while also working your shoulders, back, arms and legs.

A Stand up straight, with your feet a shoulder-width apart and your toes pointing slightly outwards. Don't drop your head, which should be in line with your torso, with your eyes looking ahead.

B Keeping your feet flat and torso straight, slightly bend your knees and slowly squat down. Don't arch your back or let your knees extend beyond your toes. Squat until your thighs are almost parallel with the floor. Pause, then slowly rise to the starting position.

Then arch your back or let your knees extend beyond your toes. Squat until your thighs are almost parallel with the floor. Pause, then slowly rise to the starting position.

Bench Exercises

Exercise 1: dumbbell military press

This exercise works your front and side deltoids, as well as your trapezius and triceps. Because your arms must work alone, remember to use less weight for this exercise.

A Sit on the end of a bench, with your back completely straight. Hold a suitably weighted dumbbell in each hand, with your palms facing inwards at shoulder height.

B Lift both dumbbells over your head, slowly, until they almost touch. Extend your arms fully but *do not* allow the elbows to lock. Hold for one second before lowering the dumbbells slowly to the starting position.

Exercise 2: concentrated curl

This exercise is a powerful builder that targets the arm and elbow flexors.

A Sit on the end of a weights bench, with your feet slightly more than a shoulder-width apart. Take a dumbbell in your left hand, keeping your arm fully extended and your palm facing up. Rest your left elbow against the inner thigh of your left leg and place your right hand on your right knee. Bend forward slightly, keeping your back straight at all times.

B Slowly curl the dumbbell up towards your shoulder, keeping your upper arm vertical in relation to the floor. Hold the position for one second before lowering the dumbbell slowly to the starting position, using a controlled motion.

Always finish the set before switching arms and repeating the exercise.

Exercise 3: seated dumbbell curl

This exercise gives the muscles of the upper arm a good workout.

A Sit on a bench with a dumbbell in each hand. With your palms facing inwards, fully extend your arms vertically in relation to the floor and let them hang down by your sides. Keep your feet flat on the floor at all times.

B Now curl both dumbbells up towards your shoulders, slowly, keeping your upper arms stationary and your elbows pointing down. Your palms should face your shoulders at the end of the lift. Hold the position for one second before slowly lowering both arms to the starting point again. Use a smooth, controlled action.

Exercise 4: seated overhead triceps extensions

This exercise works the extensor muscles at the back of the arm. If you are using plates that can be removed from your dumbbell, ensure that the collars are *always* tightly locked.

A Sit on a bench with your feet planted firmly on the floor either side of it. Use both arms, palms facing up, to hold a dumbbell over your head. Keep your back straight, with the lower back inclined forwards very slightly.

B Slowly curl both dumbbells up toward your shoulders, keeping your upper arms stationary and your elbows pointing down. Your palms should face your shoulders at the end of the lift. Hold the position for one second before lowering both arms slowly to the starting point. Use a smooth, controlled action.

Exercise 5: dumbbell kick-back

This exercise builds the arm muscles and works the elbow extensors.

A Leaning forward, take a dumbbell in your left hand and support yourself on an exercise bench with your right hand. Keep both feet firmly on the floor. Your back should be straight and parallel with the floor. Your left arm should be bent at an angle of 90°.

B Slowly straighten your left arm, extending the dumbbell out behind your body. Keep your upper arm parallel with the floor. You should feel your left arm's triceps muscle contract fully. Slowly bend your left arm again, bringing the dumbbell back to the starting position.

Finish the set and then switch to your right arm

Exercise 6: bench press

This classic exercise (for which it is important to have a training partner), also works the deltoids and triceps.

A Lie on a weight-training bench, holding a barbell above your chest. Your grip should be about a shoulder-width, or slightly further, apart, palms facing your legs. Your feet can rest on the floor or be raised as shown. Keep your back straight and pressed against the bench.

B Now lower the barbell, slowly, to your nipple line. Your elbows should point down, while the rest of your body stays in position. Don't arch your back or bounce the barbell off your chest. Hold the position for one second before raising the barbell slowly back to the starting position.

Exercise 7: incline dumbbell bench press

Perform this with a training partner. It builds the triceps and upper body strength.

A Lie back on a 45° incline bench, arms fully extended and perpendicular to the ground. Take a dumbbell overhand in each hand, palms facing your feet. Your arms should be a shoulder-width apart and your back pressed against the bench. Keep your feet flat on the floor.

B With elbows pointing outwards, slowly lower the dumbbells to your shoulders. Pause for one second, then slowly extend your arms again in one controlled sweep. Do not arch your back or bounce the dumbbells off your chest during the lift.

Exercise 8: decline bench press

This is similar to the dumbbell press, but stresses the lower portion of the pectoral muscles.

Caution

This is a difficult, and potentially dangerous, move. Use weights that are lighter than usual, and be sure to have a training partner with you. In fact, to avoid injury, use especially light weights until you have mastered the movements.

A Lie back on a bench. With your palms facing your feet, lift the dumbbells above your chest until your arms are perpendicular to the floor. Keep elbows unlocked and slightly bent.

B Using a semi-circular motion, slowly lower the dumbbells behind your head until your upper arms are parallel to the bench or lower. Your elbows should not form an angle of less than 90°. Keep the position for one second before slowly pulling the dumbbells back over your head to the starting position again.

79

Exercise 9: barbell overhead pull

In this exercise you should use light weights. It is a great upper-body builder.

A Lie back on a bench, with knees bent. With your palms facing your feet, lift the barbell above your chest until your arms are perpendicular to the floor. Keep your elbows unlocked and slightly bent.

B Using a semi-circular motion, slowly lower the barbell behind your head until your upper arms are parallel to the bench or lower. Your elbows should not form an angle of less than 90°. Hold the position for a second, then pull the barbell back slowly over your head to the starting position again.

Exercise 10: dumbbell bench press

This exercise will work your triceps slightly more than a barbell bench press does. As with that version (see Exercise 6, page 79), be sure to have a training partner present for this exercise.

A Lie back on a weight bench, with a dumbbell in each hand, palms facing each other. Extended your arms fully so that they are perpendicular to the floor. Your feet can rest on the floor or be raised as shown. Keep your back straight and pressed against the bench.

B Now bend your elbows slowly, lowering your arms straight out, until the dumbbells are just above the level of your chest. Pause for a second, then slowly raise your arms back up again. Don't arch your back or let the dumbbells bounce during the movement.

Exercise 11: bent-arm pull-over

This exercise strengthens the latissimus dorsi muscles of your back and the triceps. Use light weights until you get used to the move. If the dumbbell weight plates are removable, make sure that the collars are tight before you start.

A Lie across the width of a bench, with your knees bent and your feet flat on the floor. Hold a dumbbell by the end, palms facing up and your thumbs around the bar. Extended your arms above your chest, slightly bent at the elbows.

B Slowly lower the dumbbell backwards beyond your head until your upper arms are parallel with the floor. Don't arch your back. Pause for one second before raising the dumbbell slowly back to the starting position.

82

Exercise 12: leg raises

This is a good overall abdominal builder.

A Lie flat on a weight bench, hips close to one end and knees bent. Grasping one corner of the bench in each hand, extend your legs out straight, pointing your toes.

B Without locking your knees, and keeping your legs together, slowly raise them to a vertical position by pressing your back into the bench. Now lower them slowly, using a controlled motion, until your body is completely horizontal again.

Finish this exercise without resting between repetitions.

83

Exercise 13: rowing crunch

This move gives the abdominals a good overall workout.

A. Sit at one end of a weights bench, knees bent and feet flat on the floor. Grasping the sides of the bench for support, lean backwards to an angle of approximately 45°. Keep your knees slightly bent as you extend your legs and raise them a few inches off the floor.

B Now bring your body to an upright position, while slowly pulling your knees to your chest. Go as far as you can without losing balance. Hold the position for a count of two, then return to the starting position in one movement, keeping your back straight.

Exercise 14: seated twist

This exercise will work all of the abdominal muscle groups, and is especially designed for the lateral obliques, but also works the upper and lower abs. You will need a bar to perform this exercise.

A Sit at one end of a weights bench and rest the bar across your shoulders behind your head. Use as wide a grip as you comfortably can, keeping your elbows slightly bent.

B Use the oblique muscles to twist your torso smoothly as far to the right as you can, while keeping your hips stationary. Your head should move with your torso. Repeat the same smooth movement to the left and continue to rotate to the right and left without pausing until you have completed the set.

Exercise 15: dumbbell trunk twists

This move also works your biceps and forearms

A Sit on the edge of a weights bench, with your feet flat on the floor. Keep your head in line with your torso and take a dumbbell in each hand, palms facing each other, and holding the weights close to your stomach. Slowly and smoothly twist your torso as far to the right as you comfortably can.

B When you have gone as far as you can, hold the position for a second, then return to the starting position slowly.

Repeat the exercise, this time moving to your left. Continue alternating the movement to the right and left until your muscles are fatigued.

84

Exercise 16: reverse leg extension

This exercise is also great for your lower back, building strength without putting pressure on it.

A Lie face down on a bench or table, with your hips at one end. Your legs should be together, your knees slightly bent and your toes touching the floor. Grab the sides of the bench above your head for stability and hold on firmly to avoid sliding off during the movement.

B Now raise your legs off the ground slowly, keeping your feet together and your toes pointed, until your thighs are about parallel with your torso but no higher. Hold the position for one second, before slowly lowering your legs again until your feet almost touch the floor. (Don't let them touch the floor until you've finished the set.)

Repeat the exercise until you've completed the set.

Exercise 17: dumbbell raise

This exercise will work your side deltoids and trapezius and builds the rhomboids, pectorals and biceps.

A Stand beside a weights bench holding a dumbbell of a suitable weight in your left hand. Kneel on the bench with your right leg and bend forwards to let your left arm hang down by your side. Place your right hand on the bench for support.

B Slowly lift the dumbbell as far as you can towards your armpit. Without jerking at the top of the lift, keep your elbow pointing out and the dumbbell close to your body. Hold the position for a few seconds and then slowly lower your arm to the starting position.

Exercise 18: lying side-deltoid raise

This exercise targets the shoulder-blade muscles and trapezius.

A Stand with your back to an incline bench. Your legs should be slightly bent a shoulder-width apart, with your feet on the floor. Hold a dumbbell in each hand behind your legs. Keep your elbows slightly bent and your palms facing each other as you let your arms dangle below the level of the bench.

B Keep your elbows relaxed as you slowly raise your arms to the sides until they are at approximately shoulder height. Hold the position for one second before slowly returning to the starting position.

Exercise 19: dumbbell fly

This movement works the shoulder adductors from the chest to the inner arms as well as the flexors across the front of the shoulders.

A Lie back on a bench, with your legs slightly parted and your feet placed firmly on the floor. Hold two dumbbells above your chest so that they almost touch each other. Your palms should face each other and your back should be straight and pressed firmly against the bench. Do not lock your elbows.

B Slowly lower the dumbbells away from each other and out to the sides until they are level with your chest. Keep your wrists locked, your elbows bent at an angle of roughly 90° and your back straight. Hold the position for one second, before slowly raising the dumbbells to the starting position.

Powerlifting

Basic Principles of Powerlifting

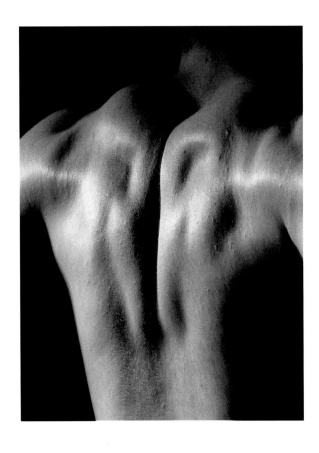

Because of the very nature of the lifts, the powerlifter does not have to spend so much of his time on technique training. This does not mean that there is no technique in powerlifting, but techniques can be learned early on in one's career and they do not have to be drastically changed.

Since the powerlifter is not permitted to move his feet during the performance of the lifts, it can be argued that his starting position is of the most vital importance because he will not be allowed to readjust his stance once he has begun.

Good body stance is essential. Their teaching is based on sound mechanical and anatomical principles and the need to discipline oneself to maintain these positions must be instilled in all prospective powerlifters.

Factors Affecting the Powerlifter

Fitness

Fitness is probably the key to all physical activity and anyone who ignores this will soon be doomed to failure.

A suitable definition of "fitness" is "the ability to perform a particular piece of work with success". Having made this deceptively simple statement, it can obviously be enlarged upon.

Strength

Strength is the foundation of the sport of powerlifting. Nothing can be left to chance and you must work on an all-round strength-building programme. Strength must be developed progressively.

Speed

Coupled with agility and added to strength, speed will produce great power. It is an important aspect that must not be ignored.

Power

This must be developed together with strength, and the powerlifter should undertake some form of overall vigorous movements such as jumping and swimming.

Training

The assistance of a trainer is vital to the success of a competitive lifter. Training a powerlifter is a question of understanding the body's plateau of effort, combining it with sound proven principles and experience. Trainers are also under stress in major competitions and a wrong decision by them at a crucial moment can mean the difference between winning and losing.

Willpower, motivation, dedication, determination and courage are all important factors that a good trainer will take into consideration. He will use his psychological expertise to get the best out of his athlete and through experience will know when to drive him hard, when to ease him up and when to rest him.

We must always strive to develop these valuable qualities together. Remember, winning is in the mind and a single-minded approach is vital.

Training and Preparation

It is obvious that, for the majority of lifters, it is advisable to look at any one year as a whole before he can begin to plan any sensible and progressive method of training. Even then, training will be quite varied, depending on the quality and experience of the competitor and his eventual goal. Therefore, the novice may well have as his aim the county championship or some other minor competition, whereas an advanced lifter might be aiming for a national title or a world championship place.

Novice Competitors

The objective is the progressive development of power, although there is also some small skill element attached to the three power lifts. Novices do not, therefore, have to devise and practise specific skill exercises.

Warming up

Warming up is probably the most neglected part of any form of training with weights. If it is important for experienced lifters, it is absolutely vital for beginners who may well be weak, stiff, unfit, uncoordinated and inactive.

The warm-up should cover all the musculature and joints. Listed below are a few exercises that may be incorporated in the warm-up:

Arms circling backwards; alternate arms swinging upwards; arms raising sideways and upwards; trunk circling; trunk bending forwards; side bending; alternate toe touching with feet astride; good morning exercise; prone lying – head and shoulders raising; prone lying – legs raising; astride jumping; skip jumping to crouch; lunges; squats; sit-ups; v-sits; short sprints.

Later, the warm up can form part of the fitness- training programme.

Training Schedule

Novice Powerlifter

Monday, Wednesday and Friday have always been popular training days for weightlifters and this seems ideal for the novice powerlifter. It allows the athlete to work hard and then to follow this with a day's rest and recovery.

Lifters should make sure that good body positions are maintained and that technique is never sacrificed for extra weight at this stage.

You should not be too anxious to increase poundages in the early stages and should make sure that each repetition is performed in good style.

Between 15 and 18 days before your first competition, your trainer should give you a maximum try out and use your best poundages as a guide for your second competition attempt. For example, if your best squat on the try out is 100kg (450lb) , you should aim at this for your second attempt in the competition.

What Next?

You are now ready to move on to a more advanced stage of training. There will be a reduction in the number of repetitions performed in each set and an increase in poundages and sets. You will start to specialise and concentrate on specific exercises for individual weaknesses.

Planning will become more important and the trainer will no longer be able to train athletes on a block principle. It is at this stage that the trainer will need to know all his lifters thoroughly and understand all their mental and physical needs.

An extra training session can be introduced and it would seem that Sunday morning would be an appropriate time. This could be a fitness training or games training period or, nearer competition time, an additional power training session.

Basic Schedule

Monday and Wednesday Exercise

	Sets	Reps
High Pulls	3	8
Upright rowing	3	8
Back squats	6	8
Press on bench	6	8
Press behind neck	3	8
Triceps stretch	3	8
Abdominal work (sit-ups)	3	10-15

Friday

	Sets	Reps
Power cleans	3	8
Front squats	6	8
Dead lift	6	8
Shrugs	3	8
Seated incline D/B press	3	8
Hyper-extensions	3	8
Abdominal work (D/B side bends)	3	10

The training cycle for the powerlifter for each major competition need only be broadly divided into two phases.

1. The Preparation Phase

The length of this phase will depend on the number of major competitions for which the lifter is preparing. The national squad lifter, for example, will probably compete three times a year: at his divisional championships, at the nationals and, hopefully, at the world championship, whereas a lifter of lesser quality may only compete twice at county and divisional levels.

Body-building exercises should play a major part at this stage of training and some fitness and endurance should also be worked on. There should be no emphasis on the competition lifts, but assistance exercises, such as narrow stance squats, narrow grip bench presses and straight-legged dead lifts, would be incorporated. This period would take you to within eight weeks of the competition and your body weight would be at approximately competition weights.

Preparation Phase Schedule

Monday

	Sets	Reps
Upright rowing	3	8
Press behind neck	3	8
Narrow stance squats	5	6-8
Seated incline D/B press	5	6-8
Shrugs	3	8
Screw curls	3	8
Abdominals (bent leg sit-ups)	5	20

Wednesday

Power cleans	3	8
Bent over rowing	3	8
Narrow grip bench press	5	8
Front squats	5	8
Round back good morning	3	8
Triceps exercise	3	8
D/B side bends	3	10

Friday

High pulls	3	8
Bent arm pullover	3	8
Leg press	3	8
Leg curls	3	8
Straight leg dead lift	4	6-8
Bench press	3	8
Hyper-extensions	5	8-10

Exercises should be performed quickly, and rest periods between sets should be cut to a minimum. The objective is to increase muscular endurance so that lifters may be able to withstand the very heavy work loads that are to follow. This is the trainer's responsibility and he should observe any specific weaknesses and work on them.

2. Competition Phase

Olympic lifters also add a third stage, called the transitional period, to their training cycle. If powerlifters were to have another phase it could be called the rest phase, but it is not necessary to label it as long as it is understood. At the completion of a competition most powerlifters will go into a resting phase anyway. The pressure is off and there is nothing to worry about in the immediate future; in practice, training will be either light or non-existent. Some even take a complete holiday and return refreshed for a new preparation phase. This varies considerably from lifter to lifter and trainers would do well to observe lifters' preferences.

Competition Phase Schedule

Monday or day 1	Sets	Reps
Squats (competition stance)	2	5
Knee wraps	2	3
Knee wraps	2	2
Bench press (competition position)	3	3
	2	2
	3	1
Dead Lift	1	5
	1	3
Straps	3	1
Abdominal work and stretching exercises		
Wednesday or day 2		
Power cleans	3	3
Triceps exercise	3	5
Round back good morning	3	5
Seated incline D/B press	3	5
Press behind neck	1	5
	2	3
Abdominal work		
Friday or day 3		
Squats (competition stance)	1	5
	1	3
	2	2
	3	1
Bench press (competition position)	5	1
	2	3
	2	2
Dead Lift	1	6
	1	4
	2	3

Sunday or day 4

If the fourth training session is included each week, it should take the form of day 2 or, alternatively, it can be used for specific exercises, such as grip work and short range power movements, i.e. half squats, dead lift from boxes and dead lift standing on blocks.

Modern powerlifting has developed from the original strength set lifting. The original lifts in the strength set were composed of the two-hand curl, the bench press and the squat. These lifts were selected for competition because they were most commonly used and of greatest importance in the training schedules and programmes of all forms of strength training, weight training and body building. This ensured a set of lifts which would demonstrate a lifter's basic strength to the fullest advantage. The order of performance of the lifts was also changed, making the squat the first lift and the dead lift the last of the three.

The bench press remained in the middle, giving the lifters a certain amount of respite between the two very heavy massive body movements.

Competitions take place both at national and international levels.

Powerlifting Exercises

The Squat

Starting Position

The bar is taken from the stands to rest across the shoulders behind the neck and is held as low down as is possible while concentrating on the lift.

The hands should grasp the barbell firmly, which will maintain the position of the bar on the shoulders throughout the lift, and should be spaced as is most comfortable for the lifter.

The head is held up, eyes looking forwards and up, and the chest is lifted high. This will give a firm and positive position for the upper body and help to establish balance and a sense of purposeful determination.

The position of the feet is generally slightly wider than hip width, and the toes are turned out. The weight of the body and bar must rest evenly over all the surface of the foot. Some more experienced lifters find that a wider foot stance is of benefit to them, but the principal consideration is judging the foot spacing so that you should feel as comfortable as possible while gaining the full benefit of strong and balanced starting posture.

The Movement

Taking in a deep breath and maintaining a high chest, lower the body by bending the legs to the position. During the lowering there will be some forward inclination of your upper body, but the back must be kept straight and you must fight against any tendency for the spine to round. The top surface of the legs at the hip joint should be lower than the top of the knees.

Training must ensure that the lifter learns to be comfortable in position so that the exercise becomes "natural" to be performed without conscious thought. In competition there is no signal given from the referee to stand erect, the decision to do this rests with the weightlifter as to when to make his effort to rise. All squatting should therefore be performed to at least the minimum position, as described above. Lifters are strongly advised not to go into the very deepest full squat position.

R e c o v e r y

When you are confident that you have reached the necessary low position that you are comfortable with, you must immediately begin recovery. It is at this point that you will experience great difficulty and you will require a lot of determination and willpower spirit to force yourself back to the erect position. It is vitally important that your knees remain turned outward, only in this way will you avoid injury. Often, due to the very strong adductor muscles that lie along the inside of the thigh, the knees are pulled inwards during recovery. This action tends to force the hips backwards, consequently tipping the chest forwards, placing yourself in a very poor stance, which will dissipate much of the leg force throwing all the weight onto the lower back. This must be avoided. Maximum willpower is required in all training for this lift to make certain that the knees are kept turned outwards so that the hips are in line with your stance and the chest is kept high.

Remember that during performance of this exercise advantage can be gained by keeping the head held back and looking up. Think of driving strongly upwards with the head.

The Bench Press

S t a r t i n g   P o s i t i o n

It is essential that the starting position is stable and balanced. (Make certain that the bench apparatus is of a very rigid and strong construction). Lie on the bench, with your buttocks, shoulders and head in contact with the bench. These body parts must remain in place throughout the lift. The knees are bent so that the feet can be placed flat on the floor. This position of the feet will greatly assist your stability on the bench.

The major muscle which is employed during this lift, and especially at the start of the movement, is the pectoralis major. Since it is a fan-shaped muscle, many of its lower fibres pull the arm towards the side rather than lifting the upper arm in a more vertical pathway as is demanded when driving the bar from the chest. To get full advantage from the action of this large muscle, your body should be arched so that the sternum can be placed in a more vertical position. In this way the lower fibres of the pectoralis major are able to pull more vertically.

Maintaining the position, as described above, the barbell is then handed to you. The bar should be gripped with a hand spacing that is as comfortable to you as possible. However, it is recommended that in order to obtain the best advantage the hands should be so spaced that when the bar is resting on the chest the forearms are near to the vertical position. It is recognised, of course, that there will be considerable variation with individual lifters and that best results will be achieved by experimentation and experience.

Lowering to Starting Position

Take a deep breath, stabilising the chest, to give a firm base for the muscular action involved in the lift.

In your own time lower the bar to your chest. This must be done under control. When the bar comes to rest on the chest and is quite still you will receive a signal from the referee to commence the press. Drive the bar from the chest with great force. In the initial starting position, when the bar is resting on the chest, it will not lie over the fulcrum of the shoulder joint but will be some 5–7cm (2–3in) forward of this point. This means that there is a forward weight arm and consequent mechanical disadvantage right from the start of the drive. The forward weight arm must be eliminated and in order to do this ease the bar back during the drive to bring it over the shoulder.

While the drive must be very purposeful, care must be taken to ensure that the elbows are not lifted upwards and forwards because this would throw too great a resistance on the triceps too soon. It will be in the middle of the movement that you will inevitably encounter the greatest difficulty. This area is known as the "sticking point" or point of the greatest mechanical and physical disadvantage. Here the horizontal weight arms are at their greatest and there is a weak link between the change-over of one muscle group with another.

The initial part of the exercise is developed by strong action of the pectoralis major, anterior deltoid and serratus anterior. At the mid-section of the press the role of these muscles is diminishing while the triceps are beginning to take on a greater responsibility in the movement.

It is here that the weakness occurs. This section of the lift is the true test of the lifter's character. As the bar passes through the mid-range, it becomes increasingly easy to complete the movement.

The lift is completed when the arms are fully straightened.

Note:
- It is essential that you have a training partner or spotter for this exercise.
- In competition, a signal will then be given by the referee to take the bar from you.
- It is important to note that throughout the lift the correct posture is maintained.

The Two-hands Dead-lift

The two-hands dead-lift is the supreme of the three power lifts, and the most difficult to master being the ultimate test of willpower and raw, physical strength. It is also the most important lift, since it is the last in competition, and a good performance can make the difference between winning and losing.

One of the most important components controlling the successful completion of the lift is a strong grip. It is recommended that you employ the method known as "hooking" or "the hook grip". The hook grip is performed by placing the top segment of the thumb along the barbell and wrapping the first and second finger around it, thereby squeezing it against the bar.

Additional difficulties with the grip occur due to the bending of the bar as the weight is lifted from the floor. The bend or spring causes the bar to roll in the hands and it is this rolling action that could break the grip. You are therefore advised to use the alternate gripping method in which one hand faces forwards and the other faces backwards.

Using the alternate gripping method, the bar will then be secure and unable to roll.

The starting position – The feet are placed underneath the bar, approximately hip-width apart. It is important that you feel all your weight evenly over your feet. Bending the knees and flexing your

hips, lower your body and grip the bar.

It is recommended that the width of grip should be slightly wider than shoulder width, the arms outside the knees. The back should be flat and strongly braced and the shoulders should be slightly in advance of the line of the bar.

The starting position must be well balanced and positive in approach.

The Movement – In this lift the weight is taken from the ground to a final position; the legs are straight, the body is erect and the shoulders are braced back. At no time during the performance of the movement must the bar stop on its upward path.

The Lift – Because of the forward inclination of the shins, the bar will be over the junction of the main body of the foot, and the toes will be towards the front of the base. If the bar were to be lifted vertically from this position, the tendency would be for you to be pulled forwards and off balance. If you do lose your balance you will be unable to use maximum force. It is essential, that during the first phase of the lift from floor to knee height, the bar should be eased back inwards towards the shins, so that by the time it reaches the height of the knees it is central over the stance. It is possible to do this because the first part of the lift is initiated by a strong straightening of the legs, by the time the bar has reached knee height the shins have reached a vertical position and the knees have moved back. Throughout this strong leg drive you should fight to keep your back strong and flat.

There will be a tendency for the back to be pulled into an arched position, but this should be resisted. The angle of the back should be maintained from the starting position, lifting the hips and the shoulders simultaneously.

In the middle range of the exercise you are likely to experience the greatest difficulty. At this point the distance between the active fulcrum of the hips and a vertical line through the bar results in a long weight arm and a position of mechanical disadvantage. In addition, there is an anatomical take-over from the muscles which extend the knee, quadriceps femoris, to those which extend the hip, gluteal and hamstring muscles. This results in physical disadvantage. A great deal of determination and willpower must be exerted to accomplish this difficult movement.

As the bar passes the knees and the lower part of the thigh, great resistance will be placed upon the extensors of the hip and the muscles of the back. The hip muscles especially, work very strongly to pull the body to an erect position and, since the rules do not permit lay back, the positive action is for the hips to be forced forwards in towards the barbell. The action is combined with a determined effort to lunge the shoulders upwards and it is in the latter part of this effort that the muscles of the upper back play a decisive role in achieving the final erect stance. It could be said that the movement of the shoulders backwards is a reaction to the hip drive forwards. However, since the movement will tend to be slow, the movement (the action/reaction) advantages will be extremely minimal. Yet again determination and a positive mental attitude is vital in performing this most difficult of exercises.

In the final finishing position the knees are locked, the head is held up, the chest is high and the shoulders are rigid.

Some of the more experienced lifters adopt a starting position that shows a considerable variation to the one previously described. In this technique the feet are placed very wide apart and the bar is gripped with a comparatively narrow hand spacing, with the arms between the knees. The mechanical implications of the lift are altered. Due to the wide foot stance the shins are vertical at the beginning of the lift, the hips are closer to the bar and the shoulders are directly over the bar. This gives the lifter the opportunity to exert a vertical pull directly from the floor.

At the same time, however, this throws greater emphasis on the muscles of the front of the thighs and because of the more upright position there will not be the same opportunity for load sharing with the back. It would appear, therefore, that this is a technique that can be employed with advantage by those lifters who display especially high levels of leg power.

However because this book is addressed directly to beginners it is sufficient that the above technique is theoretically known to exist but it shouldn't trouble you any further than that.

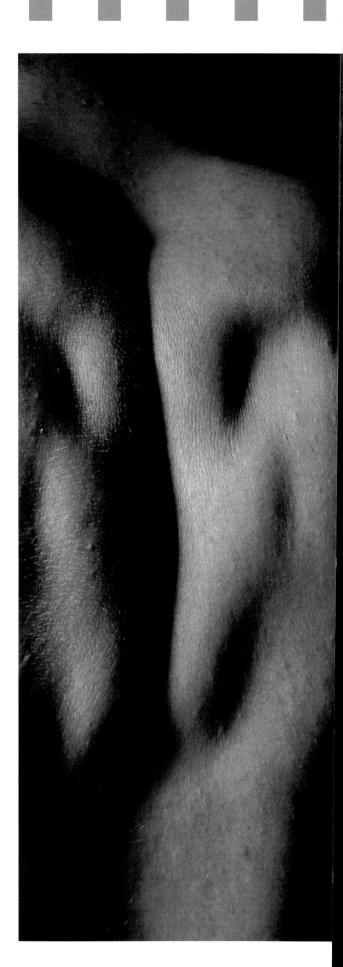

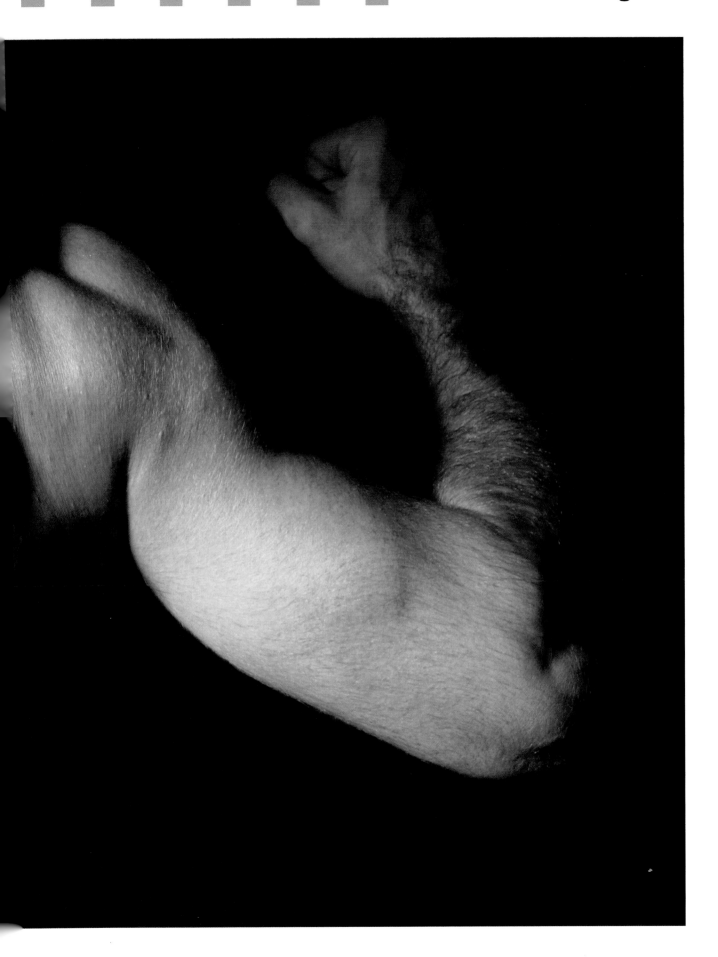

Weightlifting Safety

The Do's and Don'ts of Weightlifting

The whole message of the following section can be summed up as do it safely! Lifting weights whether it is done for recreational purposes or, more seriously as training for sports and competitions is a potentially hazardous business. So paying attention to some simple rules will help avoid unnecessary mishaps and more serious accidents.

The first point is obvious: find an experienced trainer who can help you to learn the correct way of performing the exercises. The athletics departments of local colleges and the various gyms in your area will be able to advise you and probably recommend a qualified coach.

Taking advice from people who know nothing about the sport or, even worse, have never learned to employ good techniques themselves, such as friends, relatives and other weightlifters is to be avoided.

This book and others like it can help you, but nothing can beat personal coaching from an experienced trainer.

Setting Goals

It is important to set yourself realistic goals with the help and advice of your trainer. Your personal goals will depend on your age, physical maturity and the reason you are lifting weights. You will need to consider which exercises you will attempt, how often you intend to perform each exercise, what weight you will start with and when you will increase this weight.

Being Ready

You should know when it is good – and bad – to exercise. Consult your doctor, for a start, particularly if you happen to be in middle years or have a family history of medical problems. Your doctor may have reservations if any of the following are true: you are over 45 years old; you smoke; you are prone to high blood pressure; you have a high cholesterol count; you are more than 9kg (20lb) overweight. If any of these apply to you, although exercise is a good idea, something as strenuous as body building might not be sensible.

To Kat, Catherine and Rob.

And with thanks to Glenys.

Picture credits

Pictures pp9-23, 25b, 27 © Fotostock

Pictures pp 29, 32, 33, 35, 36, 37, 40 © Getty Images

Picture pp38 © Stockbyte

We would also like to thank our model Robert Skull for

appearing in this book.